WHY DO WE ALL BEHAVE IN THE WAY WE DO?

SS O'CONNOR

First published in Great Britain by Otium Press 2023

www.otiumpress.com

Text copyright: © SS O'Connor 2023

The moral right of the author has been asserted

A CIP catalogue record for this book is available from the British Library

ISBN 978-1-7391559-2-6

Cover and end papers: Details from Pink Beach Towel by Bruce McLean.
Copyright, the artist. Published by CCA Galleries, London and printed by Coriander Studios.
Reproduced by kind permission of Bruce McLean and the CCA Galleries, September, 2022

Book design and art direction: Ash Gibson
Photo editor: Cat Costelloe

Type set in Adobe Garamond, Brandon Grotesque and NY Irvin.

Printed and bound in the UK by The Pureprint Group

OTIUM PRESS

Grand Union Studios, 332 Ladbroke Grove, London, W10 5AD
info @otiumpress.com

For Kerin and Anty, Lucy and Dom, Will and Ellyn.
May you stay forever young.

The Secrets of Life Quartet

The Secrets of Life:
From Big Bang to Trump

BOOK ONE

HOW DID LIFE END UP WITH US?

SS O'CONNOR

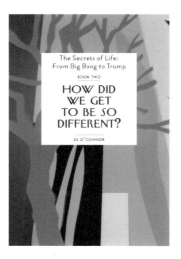

The Secrets of Life:
From Big Bang to Trump

BOOK TWO

HOW DID WE GET TO BE SO DIFFERENT?

SS O'CONNOR

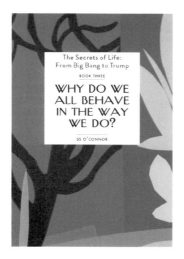

The Secrets of Life:
From Big Bang to Trump

BOOK THREE

WHY DO WE ALL BEHAVE IN THE WAY WE DO?

SS O'CONNOR

The Secrets of Life:
From Big Bang to Trump

BOOK FOUR

SO WHAT DOES IT ALL MEAN?

SS O'CONNOR

The Secrets of Life:
From Big Bang to Trump

BOOK THREE

WHY DO WE ALL BEHAVE IN THE WAY WE DO?

SS O'CONNOR

OTIUM PRESS

'Go on then, our evolutionary story almost seemed to be saying, you don't want to be told what to do, and you don't want to simply follow the instructions of your genes - so what do you want? Work it out yourselves!'

INTRODUCTION

As I moved on to write the third volume of *The Secrets of Life* sequence I found myself becoming increasingly weak-kneed at the idea of what I'd be tackling next. Looking back seemed an easy ride. I now regarded the first book as being relatively straightforward in that it had explained the various stages of the planet's story, and how the evolutionary process had come to develop so much variety and complexity.

The book had also hopefully shown how the gene directed its organisms to use whatever was around them to further their chances of survival and success. In writing this, I'd been attempting to explain how every life form somehow developed its own ways of meeting the immutable needs laid down by the Laws of Thermodynamics.

Achieving this was what accounted for the bewildering range of symbiotic strategies that were used by different organisms as they tried to find mutual benefits to save energy.

The second book then attempted to show how these same forces were also evident in our own evolution. Anthropologists and other researchers seemed to be largely in agreement that the way our cultural development had progressed was through a series of giant productive breakthroughs. By combining their views, I arrived at the seven 'revolutions' that I believed had made us who we are - and why they'd taken us further and further away from our animal origins.

These were the stages, I felt, that explained how we'd become the sentient, self-aware organisms we are today: living things that can even rebel against the instructions of their own genes.

Two of these cultural revolutions had taken place before we were recognisably

Homo sapiens. The next five would occur in just two hundred millennia, the final three in only the last 10,000 years - a fluttering of an eyelash when compared to evolutionary time.

In spite of this flat out sprint, each of the transmissions we'd made had brought with them profound changes to how we viewed the world, and to our behaviour towards each other. Possibly among the most important of these steps were the ones that helped us escape the suffocating control of Big Men in our communities. These people had sat on us for most of our history, and for what now appears to have been far too long, had behaved in the most parasitic manner imaginable.

As they had directed our lives, they'd also been taking too much from society, and keeping the rest of us in such subservience that the idea of rebalancing social outcomes had been a constant feature of our human story.

In time their iron grip was reduced. Yet the journey we'd covered from being so tightly directed to us having more control over our own lives generally meant that any changes simply brought new problems. As the last volume tried to explain, the power vacuum that followed revolutionary upsets was usually filled by entirely new theories about how we should best live in our societies.

Yes, we all wanted the benefits of group endeavours to be more fairly shared than they'd been before. And yes, too, for most of us the idea that we should have systems that allowed us to trust other people was central to our progress.

But how should we achieve this? Go on then, our evolutionary story almost seemed to be saying, you don't want to be told what to do, and you don't want to simply follow the instructions of your genes - so what do you want? Work it out for yourselves.

With the top-down, 'do-as-I-say' model in retreat, many of the new ways of putting the glue in our societies were to become known as 'social contracts'. These were the various attempts to come up with what an ideal symbiosis should look like between the boss class and what the mass of people had a right to expect. Who was responsible for what? How should we each behave? And what was the price we'd be prepared to pay for getting what we wanted?

At the core of this thinking was the belief that we could never be happy until we'd found ways of satisfying our inner drives. But if we were all different then how was that to be done? Most of the notions that the new political philosophers now came up with centred around the belief that we had to somehow get back to how humans had lived originally - in our 'natural states' in other words - if we were ever to arrive at long-term solutions. But what did this mean?

It's at this point that this third volume begins.

It picks up the story as the great thinkers of the Enlightenment are joined by someone who was going to bring a completely new approach to understanding ourselves. He would end up by appearing to contradict his own conclusions - but this would only start a further train of investigation. But solving this 'problem' would produce an extraordinary new way of seeing that there was a profound mathematical logic behind our choices and actions.

We were to discover that this same reasoning had also built the world. Further, it lay behind the behaviour of every decision that evolution had inspired.

But what was it? And what did this mean for us?

SS O'Connor

Somerset, June, 2022

A genius with most of the answers...
and all for just £20.

CHAPTER ONE

THE UNDERLYING IDEA BEHIND SOCIAL CONTRACT THEORY WAS THAT LAWS, AUTHORITY AND ORDER ARE NECESSARY BECAUSE THEY'RE NOT NATURAL THINGS, BUT HUMAN CREATIONS. NOW SOMEONE CALLED ADAM SMITH WAS GOING TO SHOW THAT THERE WAS AN ENTIRELY DIFFERENT WAY OF LOOKING AT HOW SOCIETY WORKED. OR HOW IT SHOULD WORK. BUT WHO WAS HE - AND WHAT DID HE SAY?

In the *Theory of Moral Sentiments*, the first of his world-changing books, Adam Smith tickles our imaginations with a little drama he describes as happening one evening in the late 1750s.

A well-dressed, well-upholstered gentleman, he says, is settling down into the depths of his favourite armchair, a fine dinner still warm in his tummy, and a fire roaring in the grate. Life's good. He's in excellent health, there's a glass of brandy in his hand - and he owes not a single penny in debt. His eyelids begin to droop, but rather than giving in to sleep he picks up the newspaper for a gentle catch-up of events.

His gaze wanders over the pages more out of habit than any great interest. But as he scans various accounts of pugilist bouts and grain auctions, he suddenly sits up as his eye falls on an appalling story. It's about how an earthquake has destroyed an entire city in a remote area of rural China. How terrible, the man muses, putting another slug of the rich liquid to his lips, those poor, poor people. Hundreds of thousands dead, the report says, and no doubt countless more injured and homeless.

'It really is too bad', I imagine him saying to himself, 'if only there was something I could do to help. But, it's all so far away.'

He stares into the fire, turning over in his mind the fragility of life.

'But, then again' - and before he can stop himself, a ghastly thought has popped into his head - 'we all have our burdens to bear. Why, as for myself, this horrid paper cut I got on my little finger this morning is driving me mad.'

He drops the newspaper, shocked at his comparison.

'How could I be so pathetic as to put the terrible misfortunes of the Chinese in the same breath as my own trivial nick?' Then he pulls himself together: 'Be a man. If someone, maybe even God, had put it to me that I could have *stopped* that terrible tragedy by making a sacrifice… would I have agreed?

'Sure, of course.

'OK then, since you're being such a wimp about your finger, let's say that if you had it chopped off by an axe rather than just fretting over the tiny cut you have… then the entire Chinese catastrophe could have been avoided. Deal?'

Aargh… aargh, chopped off? By an axe?

'But if it would save so many lives. How could I refuse? I suppose I'd have to agree. Well, all right then… yes, I would!'

But as Adam Smith then so ruthlessly describes our natures, if the man had actually gone along with the bargain, he certainly wouldn't have had a wink of sleep the night before the selfless loss of his pinkie. He'd twist and turn, sweating in his soaking bed, dreading the fall of the blunt axe and the agony of his mutilated hand. Whereas, in Smith's words: '… he'd snore with the most profound security' if he was never to actually *see* the terrible disaster thousands of miles away.

'But turn it round', the man continues to argue with himself, 'would you have allowed those untold thousands in China to sacrifice themselves for *you*? If they'd offered to die in the earthquake so you didn't have to lose your finger… would you agree? No, of course not.'

Quite right, a man would have to be an unspeakable monster to go along with that. How could someone care more about a little finger than the deaths of such a colossal number? Come on.

It's at this point that Smith then closes the trap. And in a squirm-making passage he says: 'But what makes the difference? When our passive feelings are always so sordid and so selfish, how come it is that our active principles should often be so generous and so noble?'

Ha. A gotcha. A nice way of telling us what we already know but constantly fight shy of… that we can never feel another's pain in the way we experience our own. And that any empathy we might have for people we don't know is far less important to us than agonising about our own problems. So, he's saying, don't bother exercising your mind with the highfalutin' philosophical solutions needed for social contracts. Because when it all comes down to chopped fingers and personal torment, or full stomachs set against the relief of the poor, don't we care more about ourselves than we do about a vast multitude of unseen losers?

Oof, that hurt.

On the other hand, we do care. Well, up to a point. And in one of Smith's most famous quotes he then says: 'How selfish soever man may be supposed, there are evidently some principles in his nature which interest him in the fortunes of others, and render their happiness necessary to him, though he derives nothing from it except the pleasure of seeing it.'

'From the standpoint of daily life, however, there is one thing we do know: that we are here for the sake of other men - above all for those upon whose smile and well-being our own happiness depends, for the countless unknown souls with whose fate we are connected by a bond of sympathy.'
Albert Einstein, *Living Philosophies*

What's going on? How do we get to grapple with what everyone from evolutionary biologists to behavioural analysts have come to term 'social dilemmas' - the endless conflicts that take place in communities between individual and group interests?

We've seen them for ourselves, repeatedly cropping up in this book, regardless of what life forms are looked at. How many times has the narrative of the different kinds of evolution been illustrated by the twin forces of competition and cooperation acting together? In the natural world every bit as much as in human behaviour, the two always seem to go hand in hand.

Adam Smith was as aware of these social dilemmas as we are - certainly in how humans deal with each other. He knew that although we think about ourselves and our own needs so much of the time, if everybody only looked out for themselves - if everyone was so selfish that they always put themselves first - then society would collapse. In fact, if everyone kept behaving that way… we'd *all* lose out.

What's the right balance then? Tricky. It's a question that humans have been grappling with for as long as we've been sentient. Maybe the great Babylonian rabbi and sage, Hillel, summed it up when he was writing at around the time of Christ: 'If I am not for myself, who will be for me? But if I am only for myself, who am I?'

Who indeed? Are we just individuals, or are we acting as part of the whole? We all know the tearing feeling we experience as the dilemma splits so many of our instincts, and just how often it seems to happen. Of course we recognise our selfish natures, but we still try to 'do the right thing'. And as for what suits the group, the human story has frequently shown that if we were ever to make progress, the balance always had to be set between the zero sum, self-server who might actually get things done in society, and the non-zero idealist who's all for sharing with others, but who could well be inadequate, mess up the job or even simply be a waste of space.

Adam Smith was the man who many believe was to show us the way through this maze. He's famous for it… but who was he, and what did he actually say?

Perhaps it's worth starting by making a couple of guesses that you know the big things about him: that he was Scottish, claimed by many to be the 'father of economics', said something about an 'invisible hand' ('No idea what that means but people are always quoting it and I nod along as if I did'), that he wrote *The Wealth of Nations* ('Ever read it? Are you kidding? It's 900 pages long and virtually impossible to follow') and that he says we should have 'free markets' ('Don't know if they're such a good idea. Lots of clever people are always saying they get us into trouble.')

Besides these though, he has to be pretty important because his head was on the £20 note for years, and someone is always popping up on the telly talking about the economy, usually from somewhere called the 'Adam Smith Institute'.

But one also has a queasy feeling that Smith is the spokesman for those smoke-filled rooms of businessmen who are getting fat on idiotic consumers, toasting themselves like the secret society of Stonecutters in *The Simpsons*: 'Gentlemen. To evil!' That may be a little strong, but there's still the vague feeling that he's the champion of an unpleasant kind of hardheaded commercial outlook. And of people who believe that selfishness and harsh reality are how to create winners in life - 'tough but fair, and let the devil take the hindmost.'

So, what's the reality? Are these impressions fair - was this really what he was about? Do people understand what he said, or just a version of it? Anyway, who was he?

A bit of background. He was born in 1723 in a small trading port called Kirkcaldy that's pretty well opposite Edinburgh, on the north side of the Firth of Forth. He was illegitimate but his father had died before he was born, and he was brought up by his mother in a small cottage down by the harbour. He was never to marry and, after he'd spent a few years away, he was to live with her for most of his life.

He was a strange child - silent, withdrawn and intensely watchful - and was usually to be found standing alone out on the quay, unnerving the fishermen and merchants by staring at them as they struck their bargains. As he grew older, it turned out that he was prodigiously clever, and he was sent off to the university in Glasgow when he was fourteen to study moral philosophy.

It was there that he came under the influence of Francis Hutcheson, the philosopher who turned up earlier in this series with his views on altruism. Hutcheson was a giant of the early Scottish Enlightenment, and the first major figure to insist on teaching in English rather than Latin. It was unquestionably his influence on Smith that left the younger man with a life-long commitment to the values of evidence, deductive reasoning - and liberty.

After he'd taken his degree, Smith went on to Balliol College, Oxford where he spent the next six years. He must have been something of a fish out of water there because it seems he never made a friend, and ended up forming a poor opinion of the English. He was punished for reading David Hume's works and, when he left, the impression most people seemed to have of him was that he'd barely ever emerged from the library.

By the time he was twenty-three he was back in Scotland lecturing at the University of Edinburgh, and then taking over the chair of Moral Philosophy from his old mentor in Glasgow.

But, by now, his childhood oddities had developed into an ocean-going, mad professor eccentricity, with weirdo habits like arguing with imaginary friends he kept over his shoulder, or startling people with sudden bursts of inappropriate laughter.

Nonetheless, he had a gentle, compassionate nature, and it was impossible not to become fond of his daft ways. Brilliant but harmless was the only possible conclusion. Utterly secure in his own intelligence, he was blessed with the most beautiful smile anyone had ever seen. So what if he got lost puzzling over a problem and had to be brought home in the back of a farmer's cart? Or that he'd fallen over backwards into a tanning pit because he'd become so excited explaining something? That was just Adam.

Then, in 1759, he hit the jackpot when he published *The Theory of Moral Sentiments*. This might sound more unpickupable than unputdownable, and it contained tricky stuff like the brainteaser I just outlined - but it turned out to be an astonishing bestseller.

Why was that? It was because it was really nothing less than an 18th century 'How To Be Happy' guide. A sort of early self-improvement manual. What was one looking for in life, it asked? How were we to lead fulfilled and meaningful lives?

The answer, Smith said, was to be 'loved and lovely'.

'Loved' was the easy bit. What he meant was having people value you, being appreciated, respected and praised, taken seriously and generally thought of as a wonderful person. Why not? Who wouldn't want that? But the difficult bit was how to achieve it.

You got it, he said, by being 'lovely' - but what did that entail?

It meant, Smith went on to describe, that we had to *earn* the right to be loved. That was rather harder to be precise about. We like to think we're pretty good, even sometimes selfless, but are we really, Smith asked… or perhaps we're just putting on a show? Are we behaving properly, or only wanting other people to think we are? Maybe it's an act and we're pretending to be compassionate and altruistic because we want

'Earn it'. Captain Miller's dying wish to Private Ryan
to earn the love of others to balance the group sacrifice
they'd made in saving him.

people to say 'oh, he's such a great guy.'

And don't important, successful types look lovely because they're surrounded by all those friends of theirs, sucking up to them, telling them they're terrific, trying to be noticed, and hoping they'll be smiled at? On the other hand, don't we all know that these kinds of big cheeses aren't necessarily lovely - even though they might look like winners?

'It is impossible to escape the impression that people commonly use false standards of measurement - that they seek power, success and wealth for themselves and admire them in others, and that they underestimate what is of true value in life.'
Sigmund Freud, *Civilisation and Its Discontents*

So, who was to judge how we should behave? Well, that was the problem, he said, *you are.*

Hang on though. You probably feel OK about yourself. I bet you do everything you can to live properly - so surely you're lovely? Ah, that's the trouble, maybe you're not. How does one ever know… because the easiest person to fool is yourself. Self-deception is never far from the surface.

But if you want to find the inner truth, Smith says, and stand a chance of *really* being lovely, then you have to be horribly tough on yourself when you examine your thoughts and actions… and judge how you live with absolute dispassion.

'Though it may be true that every individual, in his own breast, naturally prefers himself to all mankind, yet he dares not look mankind in the face, and avow that he acts according to this principle.'
Adam Smith, *The Theory of Moral Sentiments*

Now this process sounds a lot like listening to one's conscience. But Smith's wise to that because he knows full well that the voice we hear when we do that comes from *within* us - and that we're an unreliable witness. As he said: 'It is so disagreeable to think ill of ourselves, that we often purposely turn away our view from those circumstances which might render that judgement unfavourable. He is a bold surgeon whose hand does not tremble when he performs an operation on his own person.'

No, he says, what we need is an *outside* view. And to provide this he then introduces the concept of someone he calls the 'Impartial Spectator': an objective, cold-eyed arbiter that won't be fobbed off or easily impressed. This rather scary presence would remind us that we're all part of a bigger world, and that we should recognise this in how we behave... that we're really very small in the great scheme of things. However much we may think we're central to how life works, the only certainty is that it's 'not all about ourselves'.

And watch out, he continues, because if we want to make progress then we're going to have to be honest. Just as altruism is so often viewed with suspicion because we instinctively know that people can do things out of vanity, or in the hope of a reward, professing to be 'lovely' can actually make people despise us, rather than attract admiration. If one can't be authentically moral, then don't pretend to be - because that only makes things worse.

'Self-love is the greatest of all flatterers.'
Duc de la Rochefoucauld

Putting out a fake version and letting yourself off the hook can involve such a risk that it's almost better not to try at all. As the American psychologist Russ Roberts says in his terrific book, *How Adam Smith Can Change Your Life*: '... to be praised without being praiseworthy - is a temptation for the weak and foolish person, not the wise one.'

Does this imply that we shouldn't ever try to be successful? To never risk putting ourselves above others? No, Smith isn't saying that. In fact, as Russ Roberts puts it, there's: '... nothing wrong with what we moderns call success. It's the *passionate* pursuit of success that corrodes the soul in Smith's view.'

The best route to becoming lovely, Smith concludes, is to imagine how the Impartial Spectator would judge us, and what he'd think of the morality of our behaviour. But how?

Well, his guidance on the place to start is to step outside of your own mind, and to coolly assess your thoughts and actions through the eyes of *another person*. This is what Smith called having 'sympathy' with other people - what we'd now call empathy - and he describes it as the process of climbing into someone else's skin, and then seeing ourselves as they do, but without criticising their opinion.

If we did that then we'd leave our selfish natures to one side and we would see the world, and ourselves as individuals, through other people's eyes. And this process would force us to think about them. We'd view things from their point of view, and we'd almost become them, sharing in their fears and needs. If we were really able to do this, then we'd gain important insights into the impact we were having on their lives.

Smith's friend Voltaire possibly expressed the idea most elegantly when he wrote: 'The only way to truly see yourself is in the reflection of someone else's eyes.'

As he lays out this kind of worrying exercise, Smith appears to have instinctively predicted some of the 'mirroring' techniques used these days in psychological analysis. He seems to recognise, for example, the way our cultural evolution has been shaped by copying the actions of people we consider our superiors. He sees right through to our love of hierarchy, and to our awe of authority figures - and he makes us see how much we're prepared to offend our own integrity to be like them.

As he says: 'Nature would teach us to submit to them for their own sake, to tremble and to bow down before their exalted station, to regard their smile as a reward sufficient to compensate for any services, and to dread their displeasure.'

Going through the tough thinking implied in using the Impartial Spectator doesn't mean we have to descend into self-loathing or loss of confidence. Just because we're not like the people we admire doesn't mean we're bad. Quite the opposite, says Smith, don't ape them, just focus on being yourself.

What he's telling us to watch out for, is what we'd now call 'confirmation bias'. This comes from ignoring the evidence we don't like and only hearing what we do. It's a process the American writer Nassim Taleb says leads to 'narrative fallacy' - the rejection of anything that doesn't fit in with the story we want to tell ourselves.

What does it all boil down to?

Hmm, this was the bit that Smith was later to have trouble with - because he said the conclusion could only be that we had to *think deeply* about how we were behaving. And that we had to use our minds and thought processes to constantly monitor ourselves. That was how we'd end up with improvement.

Why trouble? It was because he was later to appear to completely contradict himself on this point. In fact, the whole of his next book was going to argue that the evolution of moral behaviour was a natural occurrence.

He was going to go on to say that this didn't depend on an intellectual analysis at all – and that instead of needing to be thought about, it stemmed entirely from the logic that human beings would always treat another person with respect if they wanted something from him. Philosophy had little to do with it. In other words, the way we instinctively behaved with each other, if we were smart, was bound to end up by providing a rational justification for an ethical life.

'*The Theory of Moral Sentiments* was an exploration of how human beings come to form the moral sentiments they have, and it based its analysis on what Smith called 'sympathy'… that all people have a natural 'desire for mutual sympathy of sentiments'. In *The Wealth of Nations*, however, there is no mention of this 'sympathy'; Smith doesn't even mention the *Theory of Moral Sentiments* itself.'
James Otteson, *Adam Smith*

While this new theory was all still to come, the publication of *The Theory of Moral Sentiments* made Adam Smith famous, and he now became a household name, someone who was in the first rank of the Scottish Enlightenment.

Important people were travelling long distances to hear him speak, and it wasn't long before he was approached by a man called Charles Townshend who asked him if he'd like a job. Townshend was looking for someone to take his stepson, the Duke of Buccleuch, on a kind of intellectual Grand Tour around Europe and, as he said, Smith might be just the man.

'£300 a year? For life, you said? Absolutely… where do I sign?'

'So I'm just looking around - right? - when this invisible hand of the
market reaches into my purse and maxes out all of my credit cards!'

CHAPTER TWO

AT THIS POINT IN ADAM SMITH'S LIFE, NOTHING HE'D WRITTEN SEEMS TO HAVE BEEN ABOUT ECONOMICS. SO WHAT CAME NEXT - AND WHY DID HIS NEW THINKING DISAGREE WITH WHAT HE'D SAID BEFORE? MORE IMPORTANTLY, HOW DID HE RESOLVE THE QUESTIONS AROUND SOCIAL DILEMMAS?

For the two years Adam Smith and the young Duke were swanning around the Continent, he found himself in the ideal position to meet and swap ideas with the intellectual elite of Enlightenment thinking. In Paris, Voltaire, Hume and Rousseau made a big fuss of him; he enjoyed hearing about the new Prussian political theorists, he became a fan of the music of Hayden and Bach, and he was moved by seeing the Renaissance masterpieces that hung on the walls of the wealthy families he was now mingling with.

But promenading around Europe on an expenses-paid jolly was also the perfect opportunity to indulge in what had always been his first love… people watching.

Everywhere he went he'd be out on the streets with a notebook, staring away with his unblinking gaze, jotting down how ordinary citizens went about their daily routines. He missed nothing: soaking up the different ways that members of other societies ran their lives, how they bought and sold their goods, how they traded with one another, what their customs and regulations were, whether race or cultures mattered, and how differing versions of the social contract were at work. Of particular interest to him was poring over the various ways people found of cooperating with each other to their mutual benefit.

Smith and the Duke eventually returned to Britain, and after three years in London, he headed back to Edinburgh, his mind stuffed full of the things he'd seen and heard.

He took up lecturing again, but instead of talking about the philosophical insights that might come from having conversations with the Impartial Spectator, his new thinking was based on the idea that people's *actions* were the windows through which we could examine human nature - rather than what was going on inside our heads.

> **'What we think, or what we know, or what we believe is, in the end, of little consequence. The only consequence is what we do.'**
> **John Ruskin, *Unto This Last***

As to the optimal social contract, he was now saying, there was no need to concern ourselves with guesswork about the State of Nature, or theories about an idealised version of mankind. That was all a red herring. Instead, if we really thought deeply about how and why people interacted, no matter where they came from, how they dealt with each other and the ways they lived, then the answers about our behaviour would logically drop out.

And, by expanding outwards from the motivations that bound individuals together, it should become obvious how a community, even a country, would be best governed. Don't guess at what makes us tick, and don't rely on people analysing themselves, or on telling them how to improve, was the new message… *but understand how we work by looking at the evidence.*

As he lectured and discussed his findings, he refined his views and began to write down his thoughts. Unfortunately, he'd never been a great editor of his own work, and by the time he'd set everything into the magnum opus that was to become *The Wealth of Nations*, it had grown and grown into a massive tome, rambling and hard to follow.

In it he split his conclusions into five separate parts. Within these he ranged from the underlying features of human behaviour, to the evolution of society; from the errors he believed were in the ways rulers viewed the process of wealth creation, to the role of government. It was first published in 1766 and it's never been out of print since.

Why was it such a big deal though, and why has it remained so important? What did it say?

Well, first, one should say that Smith would never have thought of himself as an economist. I'm not even sure if the description meant anything back then. What he was, he'd have said, was a moral philosopher.

And his conclusions about us? In a few lines, he believed that a close observation of human behaviour showed that if people were left alone, protected from bad men, bad rulers and bad laws, then social harmony and cooperation would *naturally arise* as we found ways of trading with each other. The social dilemma wasn't an intractable

The Secrets of Life - Book Three

headache in his book at all, but simply something that would evolve as a culture of honest dealing led society to become increasingly ethical.

The key to understanding ourselves, he said, was that we were bound to collaborate with one another out of *self-interest*, and that the motor for this was the way we automatically divided up our labour. We would help each other because this led to efficiency, and the urge to do this was as naturally occurring in us as any other 1+1=3 instinct.

After all, everything, everywhere was trying to create effective symbioses - and so were we. His conclusion was that far from this leading to chaos, if we were allowed to cooperate with other people under the confidence of good laws and firmly-applied regulations, then there wouldn't be lawlessness, immorality, grabbing, rioting, confusion and all the other horrors… but instead we'd end up with *order*. And a fairer society.

Wooah. This was knuckles to mouth stuff. But how?

He took as his starting point the argument that no one would ever produce anything, create something, carry out a service for another person or, indeed, even interact with them for long, if what they were doing wasn't wanted.

Consumption, in short, was the sole reason for production: making something or supplying something. Therefore, the only reason for doing this was… that it satisfies *other people*. This was shown, he said, by the way that humans always want to 'truck, barter and exchange'. It was both a natural and a universal part of our behaviour.

Why's that? It's for exactly the same reason that every other element in Nature does it. From molecules to cells to bacteria and so on, right up to the incredible, complex machine that is *Homo sapiens*, every successful, composite thing has always discovered that working together with what's around it is the way to resist the entropic imperative of the 2nd Law of Thermodynamics.

As I've tried to describe the process throughout the entire story of evolution, whether it's genetic, biological or cultural, this ecological interaction leads to gains. Employing the magic that comes from things dividing up their labour, and the more sophisticated process of specialisation and exchange, are the only ways to find synergistic benefits.

And, by doing this, they increase an organism's chances of surviving… and the gene along with it.

In exactly the same way, what Adam Smith was now seeing in humans was that if two parties collaborated - then they could both profit. It was nothing other than the win-win logic that lay behind the shells and deer exchange.

And, if it's done properly, each of them should be left feeling that they'd had the better of the deal. Throughout history, he was saying, whenever people managed to escape the suffocating hand of the Big Man and his cohorts from micromanaging them, they'd *naturally* develop their own social symbioses.

Smith saw that we humans differed from other organisms in two critical ways. First, we were unique, he said, in that we could take the basic mechanism of the division of labour that one saw everywhere in the natural world, and then layer on top of it our human perception of value. This was what allowed us to judge how much we wanted something - a calculation that would inevitably vary from one person to another. Not everyone would want the same thing, at the same time, even if they were to value it similarly.

The second unique attribute we possessed was that we could then communicate our wishes. We had language, and we could use this to develop and refine our exchanges. Other organisms might have similar basic processes, he said, but he had never seen: '… a dog make a fair and deliberate exchange of a bone for another with another dog.'

These were the differences that made the way we dealt with one another completely specific to humans. If people were allowed to trade their specialisms, he was saying, in a free way and without outside interference, then both sides would end up better off and the general prosperity of a society would expand. How could it ever be otherwise?

Yes, we might always have individual outlooks and act in our own best interests - but, when we did it right, then *the whole community benefitted*. Wow. This was an entirely new way of looking at how societies should be governed.

How did it work?

The logic he used was compelling. The core of the process was to ask why anyone would ever enter into any kind of bargain or arrangement if they thought they were going to emerge as the loser. No one would do that.

Just like the first experiments of hunter-gatherers bartering with each other outside of their tribes, so Smith saw right through to the benefits and gains that could come from people developing skills that they could then exchange for other things they needed. They didn't have to like the other person, or to be bound by colony loyalties or beliefs.

If people divided things up, he was saying, using their skills as assets rather than just the grunt work of general labouring, then they'd be behaving in a far more productive way than if they were acting on their own.

In the most famous illustration of this principle he described how a vivid example of it was the pin manufacturing process. A pin, he said, might seem like a tiny, trivial part of our lives, but it plays an important role. It's one of the little things that literally hold life together. Yet as he cheerfully observed, it might look simple, but if he tried to make one himself, he'd find it virtually impossible to do so.

If he dug the iron ore and smelted it, struggled to roll it out and then worked the wire with his hands, shaped it and cut the right length, he could 'scarce make a pin in a year'. On the other hand, he'd seen a factory being run by a group of just ten men, that had split the production process down into eighteen separate operations, and by doing this they were making almost 50,000 pins a day. To buy a hundred of them, therefore, would cost only a fiftieth of a 'man day'.

**How this little factory
shows what we're like.**

Why would the pin makers work together in this way, he asks? It's because the process is efficient. The customer gets a cheaper or better pin - because market competition will make them the best price possible, or the most superior quality - or he'd get them from somewhere else.

And the pin maker gets money back from these customers to exchange for the other things he needs in life. He doesn't need to learn how to bake bread or run a bakery. Baking was a skill that someone else had... so why should he worry about that when he was so good at making pins?

Even within the process, though, there were further divisions. One man, for instance, could sharpen the points while another would flatten the heads. Production could go through the roof - although Smith could see that too much undemanding, repetitive work should be avoided. Nonetheless, the collective rewards for the pin makers would come from the teamwork of their joint effort.

And in using this as his case history, Adam Smith saw right through to the very pivot of the social dilemma. What he could see was that the pin maker and the baker might appear as if they were serving other people but, actually, what they were really doing was *serving themselves*. They were acting out of self-interest.

Yes, of course, they looked as if they were putting the customer first, because competition within the market meant a supplier couldn't take them for granted. People had a choice about where they got their pins from, or bought their bread, and they also wanted what suited them. But the better the product the provider made, or the more valued his manner or convenient his service, the more he sold - and the more that everyone profited.

What was good for the customer was good for the producer. Self-interest was what made it all work.

As Smith was to write in one of his most famous summaries: 'It is not from the benevolence of the butcher and the baker that we expect our dinner but rather from their regard for their own self-interest. By getting the food from them we've addressed ourselves, not to their humanity, but to their self-love - we don't talk to them of *our* needs but of the advantages to them.'

This is the bit that critics always seize on when they describe Adam Smith's theories as divisive. Surely, they say, he's implying that self-interest is the same as selfishness? And that capitalism is therefore the dog-eat-dog process that so many people worry about? Isn't he, they continue, hardly supporting the case for humans to show the 'sympathy' for others that he said was so necessary for our moral behaviour in his earlier book?

No, he's not at all. What he's actually saying is nothing of the kind; in fact, rather than suggesting that selfishness is a virtue, he's saying the opposite. Just as a chapter in an earlier book described how altruism had a genetic basis, so Smith was explaining how the process of looking after ourselves might stem from our natural drives and desire to survive and do well, but it also leads to us having to care about the needs of *other people.*

After all, if you don't look after the other man, the person you're dealing with, knowing what he wants and respecting his wishes, why should he ever want to keep trading with you? Why would he want to be the loser? Specialising your skills and exchanging things with others may be in one's self-interest but, actually, the person on the receiving end of the deal gains by it as well.

Does this mean that when I go into HG Walters (in my view the best butcher in London) and they're so upbeat and pleasant, concerned about what I'd like, and always generous with their measures… that it's all just an *act*? That they're behaving like that out of cynicism - being nice because it suits them, and not meaning a word they say?

No, of course not. Good service, concern for others, showing an interest in people and treating the process of exchange seriously, may all stem from self-interest but, over evolutionary time, these kinds of attitudes have entered deep into our neuropsychology. In exactly the same way that we're rewarded by elevated neural activity in the brain cortex when we behave in an altruistic or sympathetic way, so dealing in a fair, and appreciated, manner with others actually gives us a positive charge.

Acting like this helps us do well in society, and the behavioural patterns that get us there can become so imprinted in our hardwiring that they make us feel good - as well as getting us what we need. We've converted a biological drive into a rewarding experience.

Adam Smith's contemporary, Tom Paine, was to sum up how rational the process of capitalism could be when free and ethical exchange was allowed to flourish: 'The invention of commerce… is the greatest approach towards universal civilisation that has yet been made by any means not immediately flowing from moral principles.'

You don't need a religiously ordered or virtuous framework to act fairly, they were both saying, just two parties who want what the other one has, and are prepared to bargain for it.

Doubtless this process is more deeply embedded in some people than in others. The sad people of Tasmania, for example, had lost their trading abilities because of their isolation, and with the absence of human interaction also went mental stimulation and the urge to find better ways of surviving.

In our modern societies, however, most people in the world view the benefits that come from exchanging things as simply part of their natural way of living - probably to the point where they'd be offended by having the logic of the process explained to them.

So, do individual activities work their way through to how society functions? Do our experiences affect one's view of the social dilemma?

Yes, they do, very much so says Smith. Exchanging one's skills, even one's opinions, attitudes or personalities in productive and thoughtful ways... actually contribute to society. People benefit from them because everyone ends up with a stake in the community's growth and prosperity. Instead of being selfish, in other words, the collective weight of people acting in their own interests leads directly to the public good.

Adam Smith summed up his reasoning like this: people have their self-directed skills and occupations, so they need other specialists to provide for their other needs. Pins are swapped for bread, for instance, with money as the balancing mechanism. Naturally, people want the best and cheapest things they can get, from the most reasonable and trustworthy suppliers - people who are aware of their needs and who will respond to them. These providers are therefore in competition for their business.

But too much competition drives down prices. And, if they fall below the production costs, then sellers would withdraw. However, if demand is high and sales are strong - and there are profits to be made - then supply is bound to increase. The market rise then attracts competitors. Production increases, and the price level inevitably gets bid down again.

What's the end result?

Equilibrium. The market adjusts to accommodate both sides of the bargain.

This is how Smith described a process that's so logical and so automatic that it generally happens without people even noticing it. It's become known as the 'invisible hand' of the market (remarkably he only mentions the expression once in nine hundred pages) but his description of how a chain of responses occurs is well known.

What happens? It's the obvious outcome - supply is balanced by demand. And the upshot is that the pressure of competition forces producers to understand their customers better and to improve their production processes and the value of their offering.

> 'What happens if a greedy shoemaker increases profits by paying employees less than increasing their work hours? The standard answer is that the free market would protect the employees. If our shoemaker pays too little and demands too much, the best employers will naturally abandon him and go to work for his competitors. The tyrant shoemaker would find himself left with the worst labourers, or with no labourers at all. He would have to mend his ways or go out of business. His own greed would compel him to treat his employees well... specialisation and exchange really does lead to morality.'
> **Yuval Noah Harari, *Sapiens***

Now, while the 'invisible hand' is self-evidently the mechanism that's acting in both a supplier and a consumer's interest, it's bound to take time for its magic to work its way through the system. If there's too great a delay, then customers might go somewhere else if they can find a better alternative. Alternatively, many a producer has gone bust because he didn't pay enough attention to his consumers' needs, or to his costs, let alone to what his competitors were up to.

Information is the beginning and end of refining this process. Reliable information is so key to both sides of a good bargain that Adam Smith saw it as one of the two critical factors needed to make markets efficient, and for societies to generate growth and become fairer. The other one was transport, for the obvious reason that the quicker and more easily a supplier can get things people want into their hands, the better it is for the smooth running of a market.

The end result of good information and well-organised, fast and properly priced transport systems is that the 'invisible hand' speeds up the process of markets becoming balanced. If both factors are efficient, there will inevitably be a dependable and trustworthy outcome for everyone.

> 'The free market is not a system. It is not a policy dictated by anyone in particular...
> It is what you get when people act on their own, entirely without central direction...

Well, that's it then. Message understood and job done. Keep markets free and efficient, so that the 'invisible hand' sorts everything out, and the sunlit uplands open up ahead.

Ha, Adam Smith says, rather disappointingly… *if only*.

Yes, of course it all sounds wonderful and it's difficult to disagree with the arguments. But was all this thinking only right in theory? Don't we all utter a loud 'hmm' because we know only too well that every step of the process he describes can go wonky? Isn't this the reason that 73% of young people in the UK recently agreed in a survey that capitalism ends up with greed and selfishness?

Why's that, when everything Smith says seems to make such good sense?

It is because everyone is incentivised to cheat. Given half a chance, sellers will mess around with what they're offering, shaving a bit off here or there, telling lies about how good they are, trying to improve their side of the bargain, or to get a leg up in some twisty way.

And sometimes, particularly when there's little information available, it takes ages for consumers to spot what they're up to and they lose out… and have their trust eroded as well.

Of course, Smith was writing a long time before things like brands or trusted retailers carried their reputational promise, let alone shared communication to inform their judgements such as consumer reviews or social media gossip. But we all know the fury we experience and the disappointment we have in humanity when we're taken for a ride.

Providers are also constantly tempted to get together and cheat by making the products worse, or by fixing prices that suit themselves rather than the customer. The butcher and the baker that Adam Smith mentioned would have to be saintly - or closely regulated - to stop themselves from getting in a huddle with others in their business and cooking up ways of reducing the effects of competition.

For that reason, he was particularly tough in his criticism of closed shops practices like the craft guilds that were around at his time, particularly when they set their own internal standards in a self-serving way, and then bid up the price of their offering.

This all made him aware of how unscrupulous suppliers could be when they put their heads together. How tempting it was to come to cosy little arrangements between themselves… what critics have quite rightly termed 'crony capitalism' in which they steal an advantage instead of acting fairly. As Smith famously said: 'People of the same trade seldom meet together, even for merriment and diversion, but the conversation ends in a conspiracy against the public, or in some contrivance to raise prices.'

And, most of all, it was obvious that governments would be motivated to cheat. They might pay lip service to 'free markets' and would repeatedly say how wonderful fair outcomes might be, but they were only too quick to manipulate them for their own ends with self-serving regulations, tariffs, levies, tax preferences, duties, quotas, price controls, monopolies, corrupt practices and any number of other fiddles that allowed them to stuff other countries, or to support their rich pals.

Adam Smith displayed an uncharacteristically bitter tone when he described how this often arose from the pressure of the merchant class: 'Our merchants and master-manufacturers complain much of the bad effects of high wages in raising the price… of their goods both at home and abroad. They say nothing concerning the bad effects of high profits. They are silent with regard to the pernicious effects of their own gains. They complain only of those other people.'

Sometimes governments even preferred to be willfully blind to bad practices taking place, particularly if they didn't want to face up to nasty problems in such things as backward regions, or unproductive industries that were falling behind. As long as they had their heads in the sand, they could duck out of having to make unpleasant decisions.

Ensuring 'free markets' was one of those concepts that government officials like to pay lip service to. They're the ones who should be protecting the consumer with laws and regulation, close monitoring and punishments - but often they don't, or are too feeble to be effective.

Back in Smith's day, he could see that employers and workers were far too often given unequal attention when it came to creating and regulating a level playing field. Producers tended to collude with bureaucrats at the drop of a hat, and yet they would just as quickly lobby them to stop their employees from doing the same thing. This was an unfairness that Adam Smith's followers were to see get worse as a Wild West employment market unfolded during the Industrial Revolution.

> **'Even Smith recognised that a true free market is a myth.'**
> **Marcus Chown, *What a Wonderful World***

Officialdom could also be lazy and self-satisfied. Bureaucrats were frequently too quick to put impediments in the way of the uneducated classes, and yet open to siding greedily with the palm greasers of the merchant elite.

They also tended to slow down growth by acting against the 'animal spirits' of entrepreneurial self-interest. This was generally because bureaucracies were instinctively defensive, he said, and spent their revenues on employing 'unproductive hands' rather than on wealth creating initiatives.

Adam Smith was always at pains to make a distinction between activities like serfdom, slavery and even the enormous number of servants that were employed at the time - which he saw as unproductive - and the productive industries that required the specific skills that led to things being exchanged. One of his principal conclusions was that only productive industry went into making society better.

This is where another of the great parallels with the natural world is so apparent. Just as both sides in a symbiosis are motivated to work together to arrive at benefits in a non-zero way, so Smith's vision of capitalism saw societies improving because specialisation and exchange made the society's wealth *grow*. The life of a community shouldn't be a zero sum game in which one lot of people won at the expense of others losing, whether they were bosses or the working man; it should be a living organism in which everyone could win.

Surely this is where Marx and the other socialist thinkers so often get things wrong? If you see society as only one side winning as another part of it loses, then there will always be unfairness. As Ed Yardeni puts it in his book *In Praise of Profits*: '(Marx)... failed to understand that the only class that matters in capitalism is the consumer class, which includes everybody.'

It wasn't the responsibility of rulers to redistribute wealth fairly, largely because it was an impossible job. It came about by everyone working in their own best interests. It was a bottom-up effect, not something that a top-down authority would ever achieve.

Smith was also alive to how easily wages could differ from one occupation to another. He recognised, for example, that some jobs were hard and unpleasant, that some might need a certain type of person, or that others might give people emotional rewards rather than just money.

Nonetheless, he got himself into a fantastic muddle by trying to work out the marginal utility value of labour. He spent a long time, for instance, getting bogged down over whether it was easier for a hunter to kill a beaver rather than a bear, and therefore how he should get paid for doing one, rather than the other. OK, he didn't get everything right.

But what he did see was that profits were a good thing if they were generated by fair competition. Or, particularly, if they were invested back into making higher quality products or an increasingly efficient supply process. By doing things this way, he said, profitable operations would ensure that prosperity grew and that society, in general, would become better balanced.

It followed from this, that wealth - like knowledge - didn't have to be finite. By encouraging non-zero cooperation, the amount of money in an economy would mushroom and everyone could be better off. What it needed was for the government to do its job by laying down the conditions that made this process trustworthy. If property rights, respected laws, transparent justice, fair taxes, public welfare and the monitoring of regulations were in place... then an ideal social contract should naturally follow.

So, how could this happen?

Information about competition, in Smith's view, was the key to making the system work. The 'invisible hand' would expose problems, people should then work together to solve them, innovation would follow, and better and cheaper services and products would be the result.

Yes, the problem-solvers would make money. Yes, too, they were acting in their own interests... but the consumer and society in general would be better off as well. Wages would rise and social infringement and inequalities would be reduced, liberal values would flourish and a moral culture with trust at its centre was bound to expand.

All good, you'd think. As Robert Wright summarised it in *Nonzero*: '... if we act in our own self-interest, we end up making things better for society. You don't get chaos, you get order and security, naturally arisen not imposed, from the ground up not the top down.'

'(Smith) realised that social harmony would emerge naturally as human beings struggled to find ways of living and working with each other. Freedom and self-interest need not lead to chaos, but - as if guided by an 'invisible hand' would produce order and concord.'

Eamonn Butler, *Adam Smith*

So, in short, we just have to recognise that the system works automatically, and to take our hands off the levers - let the whole process develop naturally and fiddle with it as little as possible. Who wouldn't want this?

Ah, said Smith, sadly it doesn't work quite as effortlessly as that. But why not?

Well, first, what results when an industry or occupation comes to an end? Pin making, as it happens, was soon to collapse as a worthwhile occupation with the invention of staples, industrial glues and mass manufactured clothes. What was going to happen to all those high quality craftsmen who only had that one skill - something that was no longer wanted? Were they to starve?

It was all very well, Smith was saying, that the individual should shape society, in the same way that a cell will shape an organism... but humans could really suffer if an individual fell by the wayside. 'No man is an island, entire of itself... we are all part of the main', he'd have no doubt quoted John Donne: we were all elements in the vast organism of humanity that was in turn acting on us, the effects of which we're only vaguely aware of. Recognising this undoubtedly lay behind his famous insight about how every single one of us: '... stands at all times in need of the cooperation and assistance of great multitudes, while his whole life is scarce sufficient to gain the friendship of a few persons.'

And, secondly, what about the inadequates in society, those people that were simply too poor or disadvantaged to learn a craft or develop a skill? Or servants with no job security, or the mass of people with no power, or the lame and disabled, or children with no one to look after them, or, God forbid, individuals who fell ill or got into trouble. What about them?

Not only that but what about unscrupulous suppliers? People who didn't take a long-term view, but who'd snatch at a profit and then disappear? Or who didn't care about their workers, or the people they cheated with dodgy goods and services? Or foreign governments who dump stuff that can ruin another country's industries? Or maniac monarchs that overspent, or crazy wars that tore money out of the system? Or the thousand and one other things that needed sorting out before markets were truly free?

Of course, Adam Smith was saying, the social dilemma will be resolved by letting people act in their own self-interests… but what was plain was that you still needed government intervention to run things.

How, then, did Smith think that the social contract should develop?

And what, in other words, was a government for?

What is a government for? 'First, the duty of protecting the society from
the violence and invasion of other independent societies; secondly,
the duty of protecting, as far as possible, every member of the society from
the injustice or oppression of every other member of it... thirdly,
the duty of erecting and maintaining certain public works and certain
public institutions, which it can never be in the interest of any individual...
to erect and maintain'. Adam Smith. *The Wealth of Nations*

CHAPTER THREE

IF ADAM SMITH WAS ARGUING THAT PEOPLE'S PRIMARY MOTIVATION WAS SELF-INTEREST (BUT DON'T WORRY BECAUSE THIS ULTIMATELY LEADS TO SOCIAL HARMONY) THEN WHAT DID HE THINK A GOVERNMENT WAS FOR? HOW DID HE THINK THE CONSTANT TEMPTATION TO CHEAT COULD BE AVOIDED? AND WHAT DID HE THINK RULERS SHOULD DO TO ARRIVE AT THE BEST KIND OF SOCIAL CONTRACT?

By the time people had ploughed through *The Wealth of Nations*, most of its readers began to rate Adam Smith pretty high on their Premier League table of global geniuses. Some even had him up there on the same kind of points total as Newton. But while this might have made him famous - it sure didn't make him any less odd. Yes, he'd opened people's eyes to an entirely new way of looking at how humans operated, but when it came to sharing his thoughts, he could still be as sticky as ever.

He'd always disliked arguing with people he didn't know well. Now he went a step further, and instead of welcoming discussion, or maybe even enjoying an occasional chat about his ideas, he took to answering peoples questions with the accusation that they were trying to wriggle out of buying his books.

None of this stopped him from having some passionate fans. And few of the groupies were more interested in what he had to say than politicians. When William Pitt was Prime Minister, for instance, he invited Smith to dinner with some of his Cabinet colleagues and made everyone stand until he'd first seated himself. 'Please, we insist', said Pitt, 'we are all your students.'

Why were these kinds of people so keen on understanding what he had to say? What had made him such a superstar to political philosophers? It was because Smith was saying that if one accepted how bricks were made and laid together, then it followed that one should also accept the wall. And so, he argued, if his logic about the way individual humans interacted with each other was recognised, then it was bound to lead to a workable social contract. And logically, this meant that the role of government would become clearer.

So what were his conclusions?

Above all else, he said, the State should clear away obstacles that were in the way of human collaboration, and instead actively encourage our natural processes.

His underlying message was that if a state's productive capacity depended on increasing the efficient exchange of its citizens' specialisms, then the easier this was made to function… the *wealthier* the country would become. This was essentially the idea of 'human capital' in an earlier form, but it was a revolutionary way of looking at what made for a successful nation and a prosperous populace. It also showed why one country might become better off than another.

Before Adam Smith came along, it was commonly accepted that a nation's wealth depended on how much gold and silver there was in its vaults. The more the better.

How did it get there? By a country making money by exporting more produce than it imported. If it did this then a nation would do well - by making others do badly. Now Smith showed that this old 'mercantile' system, with its dependence on the value of precious metals - and on beating other countries - might be a seductive notion, but it was actually as counterproductive as an individual or tribe was if they withdrew from the vital stimulation that came from outside contact.

Along with this went the idea that a Big Man or, indeed, any government, could simply tell its people what to do as if they were obedient automatons. This was the old top-down, zero sum way of doing things. It might have worked previously, but a far larger, more connected and informed world meant the inequalities of the past had bred the revolutionary uprisings that had erupted in so many countries. Why had these become inevitable? It was because people had become angry with seeing their efforts pocketed by the ruling class. They were fed up with bad leaders seeing society as a sort of mafia racket.

That model was over. Now, enlightened governments were beginning to appreciate the concept of human capital. Smith's writings were making politicians realise that the prosperity-generating potential of people refining their skills, and acting efficiently to exchange them, could be good for the individual - *and* good for the country. The smoother and more trusted the markets in which their citizens worked, the better the country did.

What did this mean the State had to do to make the nation and its citizens wealthy?

Critics of free markets tend to answer that it would 'feed the system', as if the hand of government was an impersonal breaker of an individual citizen's liberty. This is the essential problem of capitalism, so many people think.

But no, that wasn't right, Smith was saying. On the contrary, men and women should be empowered to get on with things. As far as possible, governments shouldn't be central planners handing out orders, but maximisers of human potential, creating a system that could unleash the collective talents of its people. If a fire was to be lit under an economy, he proposed, then what was needed were universally accepted rules and laws that allowed the functions of the State to act as a 'fire basket'.

First, he said, its duty was to make sure its people were in as good a shape to participate as possible. Keep them healthy. The sick, hungry and unfit couldn't contribute, and they'd become depressed and unmotivated; this would lower the public's morale and reduce their productive capacity. So develop and maintain the country's infrastructure, and keep people safe with things like sanitation, efficient agriculture and healthcare. Doing so paid off.

Secondly, educating people was key. Skills needed to be taught and any wise government should be able to see that generating an informed and highly skilled workforce was a worthwhile investment. No system would ever work if its people didn't… they had to be equipped to contribute.

Then, thirdly, the State should protect the vulnerable. Exchanging specialisms might be a natural and efficient use of human collaborative instincts, but it also meant that people could lose their livelihoods through no fault of their own. Entire industries could go into decline. Technological advances could put people out of work.

Although the use of machinery instead of human labour was still in its infancy, Smith was looking ahead to a time when many industrial processes were subject to rapid change. Men and their families had to be helped through transition periods until they could start earning wages again. Miners didn't become novelists overnight.

Last, the vulnerable in society should be protected from the worst ravages of poverty and want. Not everyone would be able to find a specialist skill. General labouring was poorly paid, and many people were simply unable to work. Smith knew that an increase in prosperity could be achieved remarkably quickly, but that the disadvantaged needed the State's help while the gains were being achieved.

He'd seen how his own country of Scotland had been engulfed in penury and misery, and had yet emerged to become one of Europe's tiger economies. No nation, he said, could be at ease with itself, or do well economically, while large numbers of its citizens were without hope, or living in squalor and despair.

If these factors all put fuel on the 'fire', then the next duty of the government was to honour their side of the social contract and ensure that the rights of its people were protected. A nation should avoid unnecessary, expensive wars wherever possible, because they ripped wealth out of the system. They also ran the risk of bringing widespread distress and hardship, particularly if the country was defeated. The State's first duty, however, was to defend its citizens and their property from bad men and foreign invasion.

Then, Smith said, it was crucial that a strong government should prepare and maintain the conditions that allowed free markets to function efficiently. There should be transparent justice, no favours given to any section of society, good laws, enforcement agencies to protect freedoms and personal security, trustworthy regulations for trade, painful penalties for suppliers that colluded among themselves or cheated the consumer, and ironclad property rights and protection for peoples' savings and investments. A government that was trusted by its taxpayers would clamp down on vested interests and ensure that its systems led to a universal trust in its leaders.

'(Adam Smith said that the progress of a society required) Little else…
but peace, easy taxes, and a tolerable administration of justice'. But these three
things were then, and are now, the three hardest things in the world to find.'
PJ O'Rourke, *On The Wealth of Nations*

Unlike the other social contract thinkers, Smith didn't give a fig whether the State was run by monarchies, military men, scholars or road menders, just as long as the hand of government operated to ensure its laws and moral principles were just and fair.

Anything was better than dictatorships, he said, or the type of vicious, bullying Big Man that hid behind a wall of hypocritical cant. Government bureaucracies should be limited in size, and be constantly aware that they represent a cost to the nation. Too large a State could sap its wealth by paying for too many unproductive employees.

As for government income from taxes, people shouldn't have to be surprised by sudden, unexpected demands. 'There is no art which one government sooner learns of another, than that of draining money from the pockets of the people', he was to write, clearly anticipating the age-old arguments that the social contract cut both ways. In short, taxes should be: '… predictable, convenient, and efficient… certain, not arbitrary, as little as possible, and the timing of payments, the quantity and method clear and unvexatious.'

Last, one-sided fiddles that countries were fond of introducing like tariffs and subsidies got in the way of free exchanges with other nations. They might be necessary for short-term fixes, but they were ultimately counterproductive. Of course it was tempting to make quick gains by hobbling your competition, but really trade exchanges between countries should be no different than those between individuals. Both sides should win.

'... markets only work within a set of rules and regulations... (if not, they) are not free markets; they are rigged markets. This is not capitalism. It is a betrayal of capitalism.'
Mathew Sayed, *The Times*

Imports, therefore, should be as acceptable to open, vibrant economies as exports. Trading partners should do well too, even though it was natural to aim at outcompeting them. Nations should want their neighbours to succeed, because in due course their people would become customers, and their growing prosperity would then spill over and increase *everyone's* overall wealth. Wider markets would lead to greater stimulation and prosperity, and anything that encouraged information or led to the expansion of efficient and fast transport systems had to be beneficial. Add it all up and it was the non-zero principle of life... but now extended to international relations.

Smith's logic meant that the system worked better in cities and 'great towns' than it did in rural areas. This was because the greater the population density, and the more that specialisms could be grouped together, then the more that interactions could happen, the more information would be shared, and the greater was the likelihood that problems would be shown up.

The quicker that people could see what needed fixing, the more likely it was that innovation and market competition would spring up to solve them. Why was that? It was because people made money from finding answers to issues. The more exposure there was, the more the 'invisible hand' would lead to better ways of doing things - and to overall prosperity.

But under Adam Smith's tough, sensible sounding writing, there was a more important message. And this was that getting the best out of people would also naturally solve the problems of arriving at a fair social contract. In saying this, he was convinced that no country or society could be happy with itself, or truly progress, if some individuals were rich while others were in need.

Yes, he said as he repeated his view from the *The Theory of Moral Sentiments*, indeed there were: '… some principles of our natures that interest us in the fortunes of others.' He wasn't saying that these principles were a wholly rational part of our make-up, but his great vision was that if the system of government ran well, then the collective compassion of a society would grow along with its wealth.

Perhaps this natural desire of ours to see an equitable split in society's fortunes came from some deeply held desire to look after our customers? Or maybe there's always been a meme lodged somewhere in our neuropsychology that cooperation is the way that societies end up with fairness, freedom and an increase in happiness?

If the specialisation and exchange processes were allowed to work efficiently, Smith concluded, then the cumulative effect would lead to open, competitive markets in which people would accumulate property and even capital. The prosperity of the whole society would increase.

Wealth wasn't a fixed amount but grew, created by humans working together and behaving in exactly the same way that cooperation in the natural world has always produced increasingly advanced and complex organisms. Knocking down trade barriers, building surpluses, solving problems, being innovative and reinvesting the increase in wealth back into society made an entire nation *both richer and more caring*.

It was an incredible, mind-blowing idea. And one that put philosophers and social theorists from Plato to Hobbes, Locke, Rousseau and all the rest of them into the pile marked 'Interesting… but perhaps not quite right.' No wonder Pitt made his Cabinet stand.

Under it all, Adam Smith was also saying something even more remarkable. His conviction was that because humans - like every other living thing - were always trying to form alliances and make synergistic gains, he could only conclude that the directional current of human evolution was also an *unstoppable vector*.

Just as in Nature, he could see that the growth of collaboration in societies was an evolutionary force. Governments could either recognise this, he said, celebrate it, and accelerate its progress with helpful laws and regulations. Or they could get in its way, impose the dead hand that came with a top-down administration, and slow the whole process down.

But what they could never do was to *stop* it.

As Smith put it: '... the uniform, constant and uninterrupted effort of every man to better his condition... is frequently powerful enough to maintain the natural progress of things toward improvement, in spite of both the extravagance of government and of the greatest errors of administration.'

'So long as human exchange and specialisation are allowed to thrive somewhere, then culture evolves whether leaders help it or hinder it, and the result is that prosperity grows, knowledge flourishes, the environment improves and wilderness expands.'
Matt Ridley, *The Rational Optimist*

You'd think that the idea of trusting in the genius of humanity and having rulers that took their hands off the controls was a compelling temptation. Yet it's something that very, very few have ever found it possible to do. But why? Why is it that this seems to be such a difficult thing for governments to do, when even the briefest of glances at a beehive, a plant, our own bodies or, indeed, any other organism in the natural world... all show that a collective enterprise can be self-regulating?

Instead, throughout the whole of human history the big cheeses have only believed in the complete opposite of this. They've fought the idea of trusting people. They've been terrified of our natural drives. Rather than leaving us alone, they've continually tried to impose their version of micromanaged systems.

When this is at its most extreme and the levers of power have been in the hands of a few individuals, whether they were Kings or Emperors, Royal Highnesses, Commissars, Supreme Leaders, Great Helmsmen, Fuhrers, Men of Steel, Il Duces, Generalissimos, Comrade Number Ones, Dear Fathers, Brilliant Geniuses of Humanity or any of the other grotesque and absurd names they give themselves, all these horrible monsters existed because every one of them was convinced that *only they knew best* - and that everyone else knew nothing.

Adam Smith may have his critics but few people can argue that the difference between his social prescriptions and these kinds of totalitarian ideologues is a few hundred million lives, mostly sacrificed on the altar of misguided beliefs and deranged egos. And, of course, people like these all have to rule with absolute power - which means that each of them finds in the end that the only way they can maintain their grip is by using terror tactics. If Smith had been invited to dinner with any of the lot I've just mentioned, he'd have been advised to have his lawyer draw up his Will first.

Why did these Big Men always feel compelled to rule like this? For most of them and their cronies, it stems from them seeing humanity solely through their own eyes, and since they're always confirmed zero summers, they view the whole of society as containing people who only want to win by making others lose. In other words, they see the selfish instinct that drives themselves as the motivation of each of their subjects, and therefore they think the masses have to be *controlled*. This means, as they used to say about Hitler, that: '… faced with the choice between changing himself, or changing the world, he took the easier route.'

Instead of this, Smith said that governments had to do the hardest thing possible - and get out of the way. As Eamonn Butler concludes in his biography, *Adam Smith*: 'Human nature is a better guide to the creation of a harmonious society than the overweening reason of zealots, visionaries and political activists.'

If history has taught us anything, it is that nobody, ever, has been able to maintain control of a sophisticated system of government by looking down on their country from on high. However extreme a ruler's reach might be, or however unquestioning the loyalty of his apparatchiks, the creation of a balanced society has to be a bottom-up process. Like the products of evolution in the natural world, that is the only way a community can arrange itself, and encourage its internal symbioses.

Smith, himself, saw through to why the centrally planned, command and control economies would ultimately fail: 'The man of system… is apt to be very wise in his own conceit; and is often so enamoured with the supposed beauty of his own ideal plan of government, that he cannot suffer the smallest deviation from any part of it… He seems to imagine that he can arrange the different members of a great society with as much ease as the hand arranges the different pieces upon a chessboard.'

And so the world has increasingly come to agree with him that even the harshest of dictators or most dedicated of ideologues can have as many informers, labour camps, political slogans and Lady Macbeth wives as he wants, but the lesson we seem to keep on learning is that, ultimately, the direction of non-zero cooperation will not be denied. People want to deal with each other. And they want it just as much as everything else in Nature does. It is a universal law.

Where did Adam Smith's great insights lead? And what do most observers think his legacy amounts to?

Well, first, he seems to have reached his conclusions with almost incredible prescience. Remember that he was writing 250 years ago, at a time when the vast gulf between the haves and the have-nots was a fact of life, when the huge majority of people had the most precarious of existences, and when there were only authoritarian societies and top-down controls.

He lived at a time when colossal numbers of people led the unproductive lives of servants or virtual slaves, and where justice was arbitrary and gruesomely unfair. Charles Dickens, for example, describes in *A Tale of Two Cities* how there were over two hundred offences on the statute book at that time which could be punishable by death. Further, there was absolutely no evidence that anything other than the mercantile system was feasible for running a nation's finances.

And yet, somehow, Adam Smith could look ahead to a time when free markets would turbocharge prosperity and provide opportunities for millions of striving individuals. In spite of every bit of evidence around him, his great brain could imagine that if a country followed his guidance and put the right laws and economic prescriptions in place, then it would blossom.

What would he have made of our recent history? In spite of probably never having heard of them, how could he have guessed that places like Hong Kong, Singapore, South Korea and Taiwan would cook up his recipes and unleash the talents of their people to vault from mosquito-ridden swamplands into economic powerhouses in just a couple of generations?

> 'While political intervention can destroy market functioning, it can also enable it.
> But markets are not inviolable, and they derive their reason for being not
> from any supposed sanctity of capitalism itself, but from their place within
> modern commercial society. Ultimately, especially within democracies,
> it falls to the state to underwrite that legitimacy.'
> Jesse Norman, *Adam Smith. What He thought and Why It Matters*

PJ O'Rourke describes in his book, *On The Wealth of Nations*, how this was achieved without the mercantile dream of gold and silver - but by releasing the power of non-zero interaction: 'Just a few years ago the common ploughman of China was thought to possess no human capital at all. Today he's reckoned to be the most potent economic force in the world. It's not because one billion Chinese peasants got MBAs.'

Tragically, it's now apparent that the belief China showed in allowing Smith's principles to run within its Communist ideology is tending to fall apart as its growth comes under pressure. Scratch such places, unfortunately, and the old authoritarianism can so easily return.

Even Adam Smith would have been staggered at how right he'd prove to be about the two key factors he identified as the accelerators of progress. With the explosion of information triggered by advanced communication gizmos, digital technology and the internet, together with the globalisation revolution that better road and rail infrastructures, sea containers and computer-controlled transport systems have made possible, the world's economy has become unrecognisable from where it was even fifty years ago.

Along the way, repressive ideologies from communism to fascism, socialist paradises, racist societies, planned economies and state intervention have all led to failure and discredited leaders. As the world has swung towards free markets - in spite of shortcomings in the ways these have been implemented - poverty has plummeted, life expectancy leapt, education levels rocketed, and opportunities have opened up. The outrageous dreams and prayers of billions of people have turned into a realistic expectation of better times.

All the Big Men that Smith must have had in mind when he was writing would have regarded his views as crazy or dangerous. Instead, they'd have been convinced that their vision was right, and that the big ideas they had about how people should be ruled were not open to argument. But as the social commentator Danny Finkelstein wrote recently: 'I like small ideas. Big ideas murdered my grandmother and exiled my grandfather, imprisoned my dad and had a good go at starving my mother to death.'

'Any definition of liberty that is not based on a right to property and a right to the same rights as all other people have is meaningless. What we have is ours, and nobody can push us around. This is practically all we mean when we say we are free.'
PJ O'Rourke, *On The Wealth of Nations*

Do these big ideas of the top-downers ever really die? No, apparently not. Every generation seems to reinvent the notion of command and control as a force for good and yet, every time they do so, they now want it to be democratic, caring, cuddly and pure. Yes, people always strive for equality, compassion, higher incomes, individual freedoms, better education, longer lives and social justice - who doesn't want that? - but, no, they don't want capitalism with its 'soulless materialism'. Equally, they don't want one-party states, surveillance and repression. Hmm… tricky stuff when it comes to balancing society's cake and having people eating it.

But why are we so often left with the depiction of Adam Smith as an icon of implacable right wing views? The image is so misplaced when it's set against what he actually wrote that most commentators seem to think it's because his solutions appear to be too 'laissez faire' for a world of confusion and pessimism.

In doing this they're strapping on the same set of blinkers that Darwin's critics did when they couldn't see how the bewildering complexity of Nature would ever have arisen from the simplicity of natural selection. The idea of organisms themselves evolving their positions, rather than some God-like authority doing it, was simply too much for them.

In exactly the same way, believing that arranging the complicated, tangled existence of humans can be best achieved by trusting them to sort out their own lives is just too great a leap of faith for many people. And yet in doing this they also refuse to look at the evidence of the successes and failures of the last couple of hundred years of history.

The second criticism people have is that Smith's insistence on trusting people's instincts for self-interest would appear to take too long to work through to solving society's needs. He was always using the phrase 'slowly and gradually' and this timeframe upsets people when they become impatient at how much human distress needs to be urgently addressed.

His maxims, therefore, can come over as working - again like evolution - in too mechanical a way for real social advances to be seen. His prescriptions simply seem too generalised, and sometimes too insensitive. And yet, as his biographer, Jesse Norman, wrote about him in *Adam Smith: What He Thought, and Why It Matters*: 'The real Adam Smith was a vastly wise and subtle thinker... (who) stood for the liberty of the individual and was a staunch enemy of state intervention. He still has a vast amount to teach us, not merely about economics and markets and trade, but about the deepest issues of inequality, culture and human society facing us today.'

But of the criticisms that arose when *The Wealth of Nations* came out, perhaps the trickiest was that people began to question whether Smith wasn't contradicting what he'd previously written in *The Theory of Moral Sentiments*. 'Hang on', they began to say, 'weren't you advocating earlier that we humans should stop always putting ourselves at the centre of things? That we should reject only being interested in ourselves?

In other words, wasn't it your message that we should live by seeing things from other people's points of view? Yet now you're saying that self-interest lies at the root of morality. Make your mind up. In your first book you said we should let an Impartial Spectator guide our behaviour... yet now you're proposing that we don't have to do anything - and that we should just let the market automatically evolve our ethical position.'

This apparent conflict of ideas is continuously pounced on by his critics. As Iain McLean says in *Adam Smith and the Modern Left*: 'Is Smith the author of the Invisible Hand also the Smith of the Helping Hand? Is the Smith of *The Theory of Moral Sentiments* the Jekyll to *The Wealth of Nations?*' Discomforting Smith and his theories became a spectator sport early on, and it's remained so to this day. But is the dissonance actually so surprising when it seems to sum up the roots of the social dilemma, and its endless arguments about whether people should put themselves first - or the needs of society?

Adam Smith, himself, appeared evasive when he was pressed on it. While social justice would emerge automatically as a result of specialisation and exchange, he said, it was bound to be accelerated by our natural reluctance to be comfortable while our fellow man needed help.

Political philosophers took it all more seriously, however, and many of them saw what they called 'The Adam Smith Problem' as the key issue in social policy debates. In particular, the German gloom-meisters of the late 19th century became obsessed with the issue, and for years their *angst-geritten* discussions were dominated by what they were to rather unimaginatively term 'Das Adam Smith Problem.'

As ever, the root issue seemed to be the confusion over whether Smith was advocating self-interest or selfishness. What was the upshot? Well, in many people's view, it's difficult to see how a close reading of his books could suggest the latter.

Perhaps the social commentator Deirdre McCloskey went some way towards resolving the contradiction when she summarised Smith's view in her book *The Bourgeois Virtues*, describing how people became *less selfish* if the political system accepted his vision. This wasn't because they were showing 'sympathy' for others, but rather because of the way free markets naturally encouraged the importance of society rather than the individual.

Social theorists also latched onto how similar Smith's logic was to the accepted views on genetic evolution. If living things were left alone to resolve their issues, they said the process of individual elements (whether they're atoms, molecules, viruses, organisms... or humans in society) cooperating with each other to find ways of forming symbioses and getting mutual benefits, meant that order would emerge *naturally* in both genetic and cultural evolution.

The urge to create synergies was fundamental to the energy gains that held back the entropic forces predicted by the 2nd Law. This 1+1=3 process arose, each theory was saying, when labour was divided and specialisms were exchanged. Prosperity, for Smith, expanded in economies every bit as much as diversity did in the natural world.

Even when he was on board the *Beagle*, Darwin had been arriving at exactly this conclusion. Like most educated people he'd have been aware of what *The Wealth of Nations* implied, but he was also reading the French zoologist Henri Milne-Edwards' papers about how the organisation of the human body depended on the division of cell types.

In an exact parallel with Smith's reasoning, Darwin could now see that cellular specialisation lay behind how the body's different organs all worked together. By doing this, the success of the whole leads to mutual gains for its separate parts.

'Ideas evolved by descent and modification just as species do, and the idea of emergence is no exception. Darwin at least partly got the idea from the political economists, who got it from the empirical philosophers. To put it crudely, Locke and Newton begat Hume and Voltaire, who begat Hutcheson and Smith, who begat Malthus and Ricardo, who begat Darwin and Wallace. Darwin's central proposition was that faithful reproduction, occasional random variation, and selective survival, can be a surprisingly progressive and cumulative force. It can gradually build things of immense complexity. Indeed, it can make something far more complex than a conscious deliberate designer ever could.'
Matt Ridley, *What Charles Darwin Owes Adam Smith*

And, just as the evolutionary process has led organisms to overcome problems by working with the other things around them - so humans act out the same decision-making processes in our societies. Instead of always competing, living things have consistently found that it's better to form external collaborations that lead them to greater security and, from there, to a greater chance of survival.

Humans are aiming at exactly the same thing. Like other life forms we're capable of displaying a range of behaviours from horrid kinds of pathological parasitism at one end right up to the most extraordinary examples of altruism. Where we differ, as I've repeatedly said, is that humans have the unique ability to alter our behaviour at incredible speeds - varying the way we act and the messages we send. It all depends on what we think will suit us.

In doing this, we're no different to anything else in life, because by trying to win we are enhancing our survival, something we've been programmed by our genes to do. As with everything else, we're constantly employing the twin strategies of competition and cooperation in our exchanges, because evolution has taught us that using both zero sum and non-zero tactics gives us the best chance of success.

So, does one win by beating other things? Or do we come out on top by collaborating, so that everything wins - including ourselves? These are the questions we humans have constantly tried to answer. And it's doing this that has led us to make our endless decisions, depending on what we're trying to achieve, who we're dealing with, and what suits us best at a particular moment.

Every other life form makes similar choices - but their decisions are the result of mutations. And this means that they arrive at them blind, and once they've taken up a position they're then stuck with the outcome. This, sadly, is the cause of their inevitable undoing because it ultimately drives them to extinction - something that happens because they can't change quickly enough to get out of trouble when the competition or the environment is moving against them.

OK, but what has Adam Smith got to do with this biological landscape? We're not trading all the time, you're thinking. Surely what he's talking about simply applies to commercial processes?

Mmm, if only. In fact, we're trading pretty well every second we're awake. Every action we take is based on an intention, however little we're aware of it. We're trading every aspect of our personalities and desires to get what we want, and we do this by recognising each others' needs, and sometimes choosing to meet them with our own offerings. We're selling ourselves in exactly the same way that we might sell our wares, our services or our specialisms. To do this we're sometimes collaborative, sometimes helpful, and sometimes not; sometimes we're honest, sometimes we plot or bluff, dissemble, act and pretend.

And like everything else, we're all part of the great directional current of evolution: a process that favours our family and kin, helps others by dividing up tasks, respects social hierarchies or purposely rejects them. We can conform to expectations or become tricky, be trusting or not, be reliable or cheat. Yet we're always on the lookout to gain an advantage if we think we can get away with it.

Like every other living thing, we're creating attachments, associations and symbioses, but in our case we're then able to break them. We never stop guessing at what people are thinking. Or imagi ning what the other person thinks *we're* thinking, speculating on how they're going to respond, sometimes being cooperative but only because we're expecting reciprocity, and every minute of every day, we're *trading… trading… trading*.

> 'Work, even social life, is a constant stream of decisions… The common element
> in these situations is that you do not act in a vacuum. Instead, you are surrounded
> by active decision-makers whose choices interact with yours. This interaction has
> an important effect on your thinking and actions.'
> Avinash Dixit and Barry Nalebuff, *Thinking Strategically*

The result is society. Out of this chaos and confusion comes order and morality. To repeat Richard Dawkins great one-liner that we are the only species that has: '… evolved to the point where we are capable of rebelling against our selfish genes.' We don't have to follow the instructions of our hardwiring, nor of our genetic instincts. Only we, among the billions of organisms that have lived on earth, have been able to weigh the evidence, think about what works best for us, and then come to our own choices

And so, when we look at the unreal mass of nearly eight billion people on the planet, all acting in their own self-interests, what do we see? Each of us may have been programmed for survival and success and yet, to repeat Adam Smith's famous phrase, each one of us: '… stands at all times in need of the cooperation and assistance of great multitudes, while his whole life is scarce sufficient to gain the friendship of a few persons.'

> 'Another wholly new recognition is the extent of the decentralisation of power.
> We now know that Adam Smith was right when he said that simply letting people
> trade their specialisms in an unchecked or ordered way doesn't lead to chaos.
> On the contrary, it leads to non-zero sum behaviour and from there to prosperity.'
> Robert Wright, *Nonzero*

What, then, are we trying to do? If the process of dealing with each other is automatic, what are the instinctive *rules* we're each following that are balancing our zero sum drives against the non-zero opportunities we all know are available? How much, and when, should we compete and how much, and when, should we cooperate?

In a world in which our preoccupation to succeed as an individual is balanced by the gains we know are possible from helping society work better, or even by cheating and taking more than one's put in, are we able to analyse human behaviour and conclude on a prescription for how we should respond in different situations?

Well, someone was now going to come along, two hundred years after Smith's great insights, who was going to answer these questions. Like him he came from an academic background, but his work would begin exposing why Das Adam Smith Problem was *not* a contradiction. More than that, he was going to start a new branch of science that would illustrate the mechanisms that living things use to make the *right decisions* in the great game of life. Like Adam Smith, he was a complete original, and again like Smith, he was an astonishing genius.

John von Neumann on the left with one of his early computers.
Benedict Cumberbatch on the right playing Alan Turing in
The Imitation Game. In reality, von Neumann worked with Turing
when he was doing his PhD at Princeton.

Unlike him, however, he was someone who was convinced that the way to find out what the best behavioural choices should be… could be arrived at *mathematically.*

His name was John von Neumann and he was not only a brilliant thinker, but as befits the man who's recognised as the father of the digital computer, he was convinced that if he could just shake the numbers enough with computer simulations of the possibilities… then the truth would drop out.

His belief was that if one could describe decision-making situations, and set alternative options as questions, then it must be possible to replicate evolutionary time and see what came out best. This meant, he was to say, that the results would actually show *which strategies won in life*. And why. Woah.

Von Neumann's new science has come to be known as game theory, even though this wasn't perhaps the wisest description. The name understandably leads people to think that it's either a trivial process, or that it's something to do with the irritating way certain people 'play mind games'.

But that wasn't von Neumann's intention at all. Instead, he was saying, if we treat life like a game, with rules and players' moves - then we can analyse what it takes to win.

'Do you mean like chess?' someone once asked him. 'No, no' he replied, 'chess is not a game. Chess is a well-defined form of computation. You may not be able to work out the answers, but in theory there must be a solution, a right procedure in any position. Now, real games are not like that at all. Real life is not like that. Real life consists of bluffing, of little tactics of deception, of asking yourself what is the other man going to think I mean to do. And that is what games are about in my theory.'

Von Neumann and the other great brains that were going to come after him now set out to investigate many of the questions about how choosing one's behavioural tactics could decide whether individuals, groups and, indeed, whole species would survive or go extinct.

Above all, game theory was going to show how *cooperation would naturally evolve* between living things, and how this coexistence would lead to order, balance, trust, hierarchies and gains.

It was going to show what the great directional forces were in life, and how these shaped genetic, biological and cultural evolution.

Really? How?

The Prodigal Son. A wonderful message... but what's the fellow on the right thinking about it all?

CHAPTER FOUR

JOHN VON NEUMANN? HARDLY A HOUSEHOLD NAME, IS HE? BUT THEN, NOT MANY MATHEMATICIANS EVER BECOME CELEBRITIES, EVEN IF THEY DO ACHIEVE A GODLIKE STATUS AMONG THEIR PEERS. YET VON NEUMANN'S RECKONED TO BE THE SUPERSTAR ORIGINATOR OF GAME THEORY - SOMETHING THAT'S OFTEN SEEN AS BEING THE KEY TO EXPOSING THE SECRETS OF LIFE. BUT WHAT IS IT EXACTLY?

Never heard of John von Neumann? Relax, my guess is that most of us would be in the same boat. Yet he's regarded as a giant among mathematicians, a chateau-bottled genius, and that only his early death denied him the multiple Nobel prizes he'd been expected to win. No doubt if he had lived, he would have become more widely known.

Instead, he tended to stay in the kind of shadows where he was most respected. How to sum him up? Well, above all, he was an astonishing academic polymath: a quantum physicist, one of the lead developers on the Manhattan Project, arguably the most important of the pioneers of the digital revolution (your computer almost certainly runs on what's known as 'von Neumann architecture') and the originator of any number of brilliant mathematical proofs.

But he was also a close confidante of presidents, and an adviser to the many think tanks and Washington political consultancies that sprang up after the Second World War. These were the kind of places where his views could silence a room. In later life, a fatal illness left him wheelchair-bound and this, together with his ever-present smiling good humour and *mitteleuropa* accent, led to him becoming one of the models for Stanley Kubrick's *Dr Strangelove*.

Born in Budapest in 1903, (natch, there's a gag among scientists that reworks Newton's famous line by saying: '... if I can see so far, it is only because I have stood on the shoulders of Hungarians') he was a child prodigy before he turned into an adult prodigy. He had what's called an eidetic memory, a complete recall of everything he'd ever read, word for word, as well as a voracious appetite for knowledge.

Besides a mastery of any number of scientific subjects, he was a noted historian,

Von Neumann was in a wheelchair during his final illness,
seen here in 1956 receiving the Congressional Medal of Freedom
from President Eisenhower. His wife Klara said of him:
'Johnny could count everything except calories'. Peter Sellers as
Dr Strangelove is in a similar wheelchair on the right.

a classicist, an expert on Byzantine art, and a linguist, hopping fluently from the ancient languages to half a dozen modern ones. His early years were spent casually stuffing degrees and doctorates up his jumper with such amazing precocity that few people were surprised when he was elected as the youngest ever professor in Germany.

In the early 1930s Princeton University in New Jersey decided it was going to put together a sort of academic supergroup - rather like the *galacticos* of Real Madrid - to be called the Institute for Advanced Studies. It wasn't long before von Neumann was approached to join it; Albert Einstein already had, Paul Dirac came a little later, and then Robert Oppenheimer, Kurt Godel and a host of other unreal superbrains. But even among this kind of cranial firepower he stood out. His restless sense of enquiry and lightning-fast mind would often leave even the most brilliant of his contemporaries bemused and, occasionally, a little intimidated.

It was during these years that he began to be called 'the best brain in the world', or sometimes even 'the cleverest man who ever lived'. Eventually a joke took root that he was actually an alien intelligence, sent down to make a study of the human race. Then, the gag ran on, he'd liked it here and had stayed, integrating with us so successfully that he'd even managed to imitate the ways of the feeble earthling.

'I have sometimes wondered whether a brain like
von Neumann's does not indicate a species superior to that of man.'
Hans Bethe, *1967 Nobel Prize winner in Physics*

The odd thing about von Neumann was that he was the antithesis of the timid academic introvert of popular literature. Instead, he was amused and amusing, upbeat, a lover of smutty jokes, great company, and always beautifully and carefully dressed. Only his driving was nutty professor stuff, and a junction on the Princeton campus became known as 'Von Neumann Corner' for the multiple prangs he'd had there, usually while cruising along with one hand on the wheel and the other holding a book.

His students loved him, and he was an approachable, charming man, usually laughing as he sprayed his opinions around on any number of subjects. Never superior, he always appeared to be interested in what others had to say and was generous with his time... particularly if it involved parties and epic quantities of cocktails.

But there was one thing he was useless at. And it drove him mad because it was his great passion.

He was a hopeless poker player.

Why was that, he'd constantly wonder as he scratched away at his inadequacy? He'd never come second at anything, and yet time after time he'd find himself losing his shirt to people with a tenth of his IQ. But instead of growing frustrated, he became increasingly fascinated by the role that deception played in winning the pot.

Bluffing, and calculating whether others were being misleading, were evidently more important than logical reasoning... but did this necessarily mean that there wasn't a rational way to play?

He could see that the game was a distilled version of how humans interacted in life, but goodness knows, no one had ever managed to get to the bottom of that. On the other hand, perhaps if he could come up with insights into the best way to play in games like this, in which similar sorts of second guessing were involved, then maybe he could shine a light on how to win in the great hullabaloo of human existence?

But why poker? And why 'Texas holdem' in particular, in which there was a mix of face up and face down cards on the table? It was because only a fraction of the information needed to make one's betting decisions was out in the open and available to all the players. The rest was hidden. As von Neumann always said about board games like chess and Go, the information in these was 'perfect' in that the position of the pieces and the strength of each other's approach was obvious to both players. That's why he thought of them more as computations.

On the other hand, poker was like real life in that we bumbled along with *imperfect* information, doing our best to make sense of what was available, and yet watching each other like hawks to see whether other people were making more of things than we were.

It was evident that the best players weren't those that could simply calculate the odds, even though this was a basic requirement. What mattered far more were the conclusions people came to about the actions of the various players. How were others trying to get an advantage by deceiving the table? How much were they deciding who the weak players were, and then forming temporary coalitions to pick on them?

If poker was like life, to what degree was one following a predetermined way of playing, or just responding to what the other man was doing? And, was this fellow trustworthy, or was he cheating? Could he be believed, or not? What did he think you were up to - and what did he think you thought he was up to?

Mastering these mental processes of ours seems to be a peculiarly human ability. Oddly enough, I know something about this because for a time I was the Chairman of one of the world's largest online gambling companies. We were a listed company and our investors would question us on whether it wasn't possible for computers to play multiple games of poker at once, and so to keep scooping the pot.

We had to repeatedly respond that even though a number of programmes could now beat the world's finest chess players, no similar approach could yet hope to defeat the innate brilliance of the best human players at poker. These types, we said, had the ability to succeed at games which only had imperfect information, in which no artificial intelligence could replicate the bluffing that had such a key role.

The military strategists in John von Neumann's Austro-Hungarian background had asked themselves similar questions when they were speculating on an enemy's options. They'd often explored these issues with *Gesellschaftsspiele*, he recalled - parlour games - that they used to weigh up the different tactical routes open to the warring parties.

Like them, von Neumann now began to turn his great intelligence to exploring whether he, too, could use the same kind of games to weigh up life strategies. Was it possible, he wondered, to find the optimal approaches needed to make decisions in a world that was so full of uncertainties?

But what did that mean? What kind of tactics did this imply?

Well, take the example I mentioned in the last book about how you could go about dividing a cake between two squabbling small boys. I said you might be holding the knife, but you were hardly in charge. Instead, you'd be standing there, listening to the racket they were making and gloomily wondering how you'd ever cut the damned thing into perfect halves.

The only certainty you could rely on was that neither of the little fellows would ever settle down when you asked them to decide which piece they wanted. Whichever of them made the first choice, the other would howl that this meant he'd be getting a few crumbs less. How were you ever to get them to agree that they'd both been fairly treated?

Suddenly you realise that it's exactly their implacable hostility towards each other that's your opportunity for peace. Because you view them as cunning and suspicious opponents, you decide you're not going to divide the cake at all. Instead, you give the knife to one of the boys and tell *him* to cut it, and then to let the other one choose which piece he'll take. Neither of them can now complain. Each of the boys will have become responsible for the outcome. Both will be making interlinked decisions.

How similar this is to the kind of fundamental choices that surround us in life. Even in Nature, every single organism is making mutational 'decisions' about their attributes and behavioural strategies... but they're doing it in a world in which everything else is also endlessly being altered by the same process. This is how things survive.

These continuous decisions determine how evolution works, and therefore why different life forms end up either staying alive long enough to reproduce… or giving in to death and eventually extinction. This is how successful things win, even though doing so might depend on a random process.

Humans, however, have a degree of control as they weigh things up and come to their decisions. And finding solutions to these kinds of shifting situations was what von Neumann now turned whatever energies he could spare from developing the Atom Bomb. The idea of studying our behaviour through what he termed 'game theory' began to form in his mind - something he saw as the study of competition between reasoning but potentially deceitful people.

First of all, though, how would individuals behave if they - like organisms in the natural world - were rational, cold-hearted opponents who were *only focussed on winning*?

'Game theory is all about strategizing. It's about making the best
decisions you can - how to go about choosing what to do.'
Edward Rosenthal *The Complete Idiot's Guide to Game Theory*

Yes, of course, he could see that the process would involve a psychological element because that was part of how humans approached situations and made our choices. But what led to that psychology? Perhaps, von Neumann wondered, there'd be a logic behind it that would become apparent if one applied mathematical analysis?

Hang on a moment… are we really being asked to imagine that the way children divide a creamy pastry can give us a worthwhile insight into how we arrive at our life decisions? It looks too trivial, doesn't it?

And yet, is this kind of analogous approach so odd when you think that humans have always described their ideal behaviour in terms of meaningful little stories? These often come in the form of fables or allegories but their intention is to involve our imaginations, and then to leave us with a big message about what the right and wrong paths are to take.

Take the parable of the Prodigal Son as an example. In Rembrandt's sublime painting of 1669, it's impossible not to be moved by the father's tender forgiveness of his wayward son, and the joy of the moment as he returns to him. These two people are in the picture's foreground while, behind them, float a couple of shadowy figures that Rembrandt is thought to be using to represent motherhood and moral authority. They're watching on as the old man illustrates the Christian ideal of merciful human sympathy.

But who's the person standing on the right, staring down at the drama with a mixture of disapproval and uncertainty? Scholars tell us he's the naughty one's older brother, the Unprodigal Son. And when the high emotion and sobbing had died down a bit, he'd later confront his father about what was going on.

How come, he'd ask, that he'd been slogging away all these years, being obedient to the old man, building up the family business and never giving anyone a moment's anxiety… and now this? How was it that the minute his brother came back - having done nothing to help for years - he'd been forgiven and rewarded with a huge feast of a fatted calf when he, the good and loyal one, had never had so much as an old goat?

Religious and moral teaching so often works like this. A story or image is designed to give us a snapshot of life and then to deliver an idealised lesson about what it means.

But this is only rarely followed up with a wider picture. Nonetheless, the kind of actions that parables depict can often involve collateral damage, and St Luke answers the Unprod's questions by having the father say: 'It was appropriate to celebrate and be glad, for this, your brother was dead, and he is alive again. He was lost and is found.'

Of course, we all understand the deeper meaning. And game theory is designed to come up with similar insights. But where its mathematical exploration differs from these simple stories is that it attempts to go further than just making a moral judgement.

It sets out to ask: '*...what happens next?*'

As an example, take another look at the painting. How are the different people going to behave? Who's going to win?

When they all wake up with thick heads the next day, does Unprod cooperate with Prod or does he try to freeze him out? Is he nice or is he competitive? On the other hand, will Prod collaborate with Unprod? Or has he lost the ability to work? Perhaps he's now emboldened into arrogant laziness by imagining that his father will forgive him anything? Or maybe the two of them will get along like a house on fire, and live in harmony for the rest of their days? Or perhaps they'll work together for a bit - but is it possible that each would be looking for opportunities to get the other one into trouble?

This is real life in action. People tend to behave in cooperative, non-zero sum ways if it suits them - or if they think they have to for some reason. But defection is never far from the surface. An advantage is always around the corner if you're on the lookout to be vengeful, particularly if you think you've been treated unfairly. This was how the small boys were with their rancorous animosity or, indeed, how symbiotic unions work in Nature with the tensions of their mutual dependence. Inbuilt hostilities are bound to come about when things are stuck with each other.

This is the province of game theory. It may be a branch of mathematics, but it sets out to fathom how people should behave, and what decisions would best suit them. By using simplified versions of the world, game theory asks if it's possible to predict how people should play to win.

Would they be better off, for example, always making the same choice (like forever picking 'tails' if one's playing a coin tossing game) or should they sometimes decide on using a number of alternative approaches - what's known as a 'mixed strategy'.

'The theory of games is a theory of decision-making. It considers how one should make decisions and, to a lesser extent, how one does make them... Some involve deep thought while others are almost automatic.'
Morton D. Davis, *Game Theory: A Nontechnical Introduction*

It is, in short, the mathematical study of interactions: of seeing what decisions people, or organisms, should choose if they want to come out on top when they're choosing how to behave with others around them. Sometimes, for example, they'll act in a zero sum way and try to win by making the other side lose. Sometimes they'll decide to behave cooperatively, employing a non-zero sum approach, in which case they'll be seeing the process of winning as one of helping everything win - including themselves.

Then again, sometimes they might appear to be doing this, but actually they're biding their time until they can get an advantage by suddenly cheating when they've lulled the other side into trusting them. This is what game theorists call '*defecting*'. In summary, the whole process is actually not unlike how poker is played.

John von Neumann was convinced that he could pick this wildly complicated picture of strategic interaction apart. He believed he could find mathematical models that would have applications wherever rational decision-making was in play... whether this involved human behaviour, the way organisms made ecological attachments, the mechanics of social sciences or, even, the conflict of nations.

His first thought was that its most obvious application would be in the field of economics, and he took his ideas to a Princeton colleague called Oskar Morgenstern, a world-famous Austrian economist. Their collaboration produced an early article and then a book published in 1944, titled *The Theory of Games and Economic Behavior*. This examined the outcomes of games involving several players by ascribing points to the different choices, and then looking to see whether the scores - what were termed the 'utility' that the players achieved from their decisions - could illustrate some underlying truths.

The result was tricky stuff: page after page of complex mathematical workings and formulas that looked to discover axiomatic theories of expected utility. Von Neumann's biographer, William Poundstone was later to describe it as 'one of the most influential and least read books of the twentieth century.'

Many of its arguments dealt with two person, non-cooperative, zero sum games in which von Neumann explored how people could best look after their interests when they were playing in completely cold-blooded opposition to each other. Why did he particularly focus on this? It was because he'd already provided the proof for it in 1928, in a theorem that had become known as the 'Minimax' principle.

In this, von Neumann showed that if you had two players, both of whom were *utterly committed to beating each other*, then they'd quickly act 'to minimise their maximum exposure'. In other words, they'd reach an equilibrium point at which neither player would be incentivised to change his position. It was the rational outcome from which two individuals, locked in conflict, took up positions from which neither could expect to do any better.

Was that it then? Had the greatest mind in the world really come up with the cast iron proof that an unremitting collision of interests meant that neither side would reach out to the other? That if you only viewed life in terms of winning or losing, then you were logically condemned to never trust anyone to cooperate?

Well, yes, that's pretty much exactly what he was saying - and what a depressing picture it painted. But did we really deserve such a bleak insight into our conduct? After all, there aren't many occasions when human interests are so completely opposed. When they are, von Neumann had to be right - because you'd actually be a fool to do anything other than think about yourself at that point. Is that realistic, though? Will people really not cooperate?

There are some well-known examples. Total war is obviously the most ghastly version of it. Utterly horrible people are another. For an insight a little nearer to home, however, take the events that played out in March 2008 on Golden Balls, the daytime TV quiz.

Ha ha, you're probably thinking, how silly. Perhaps so, but nevertheless, the episode provides an interesting case history, even if it makes for difficult viewing. If you can bear it, watch the awful events unfold on the YouTube Golden Balls video and see how it completely illustrates the Minimax principle (and why it led to such a flurry of doctoral dissertations).

The rules of the game don't really matter as much as what happens in the final psychodrama. It was then that the quizmaster, the comedian Jasper Carrot, addressed the two contestants on how they could decide whether one of them tries to win the final prize of £105,000 *alone* - or whether they'll negotiate a settlement between them so they could share it.

'This is this serious life-changing money', he says, as he repeats the well-known instructions. After they've had some time to negotiate, the two contestants both have the opportunity to choose the 'split' ball, in which case they'll split the huge prize between them.

Or, alternatively, they can open the 'steal' ball, in which case, if the other had chosen 'split', then the 'steal' person wins the pot, and the losing person... 'goes home with nothing'. And if they both choose 'steal'? Then neither of them would get anything. Having completed this round-up, Carrot suggests that the two of them 'have some talking to do'. And so they embark on trying to find a deal.

The first contestant opens by saying: 'I am going to split this... £50,000! It's unbelievable! I'm very, very happy to go home with £50,000.'

The second replies: 'You're telling me you're going to 'split'?'

'Yes. If I 'stole' from you, every single person over there (the studio audience) would run over and lynch me.'

The other agrees. 'There's no way I could go home... Everyone who knew me would just be disgusted if I 'stole'. Pleeeease!'

'I can look you straight in the eye and tell you I *am* going to 'split'', guarantees the first of them again.

What happens? I think you can guess. The first poor sap is as good as his impassioned pleading and plays 'split' when he has to choose first. The other, horribly, understands only too well the 'Minimax' principle that both of them should have played 'steal', even if it meant as von Neumann had always concluded, that: 'avoiding the worst is the best that you can hope for.' The ball is opened. 'Steal' is the play. The contestant who played second gets everything, the other nothing.

Of course, you might well say, when you can take your hand down from your mouth, it should be clear that when two people's interests are completely opposed - and, critically if it is a *'one-time' game*, a single episode that ends there - then there can only be one logical way of playing. Reputations don't matter if the contestants are never going to see each other after an incident like this. Anything else has to be the wrong approach. To trust someone under such one-off, cliff edge circumstances is irrational.

'There is no solution that achieves reciprocal cooperation in a one-time game. Only in an ongoing relationship is there an ability to punish, and thus a stick to motivate cooperation.'

Hardly surprisingly, John von Neumann inspired much the same kind of despair about human behaviour that you'll no doubt be feeling yourself. It's not pleasant to be faced with the hard evidence that we're so self-serving.

Does this mean that the ruthless, rational player will always either pick on an irrational guy, or else find himself locked in a stalemate with someone who thinks like himself? Will the logical player only beat an erratic madman; maybe someone who's not paying attention, or a soft-hearted, self-deluding person who's hoping for some kind of cooperation?

Yup.

People were naturally dismayed by von Neumann's theorem when it appeared. However much it may have accorded with our real life experiences, the mathematical proof was very disheartening.

David Hume had similarly disappointed people two hundred years before this when he'd said much the same thing in his *Treatise on Human Nature*. In it, he'd described how an old farmer always refused to assist his neighbour in case he wasn't helped in return when it was his turn to need an extra pair of hands. His lack of trust meant that both of them would always struggle.

Wait a minute though. Everywhere around us there's the evidence that the exact opposite to this is happening. Wherever one looks, people and organisms *are* cooperating. Von Neumann's proof depended on the two people being in complete opposition - but how did life get out of this jam? How could things get to the point where some kind of *trust* could be established, so that the gains that come from cooperation could be shared out for the parties' mutual benefit? Surely competition in life didn't always have to be so completely zero sum?

Perhaps.

First, though, let's turn to you. How do you think you'd behave in this kind of situation? Maybe a little test will tell us how your mind works.

So imagine you're one of, say, fifty people who have been recruited by an eccentric multi-millionaire for an experiment. You're all put in a large room where a researcher addresses you:

'Listen everybody', he says, 'each one of you will be guaranteed to get £10,000 if you can all stay quiet for an hour! But, but, but... if someone breaks the silence by shouting out, then that person will get £5,000 and everyone else will get *nothing*. OK, the time starts... now.'

Of course, you and your new pals sit there, smiling at each other. This is the easiest money any of you will ever earn. Ten grand for an hour's work. Fantastic. The minutes tick by. Then you start taking a good look at the other people. And the closer you do this, the less you like what you see. That woman looks odd, you think, a bit weird in the way she's staring about herself, gulping all the time. And that fellow over there, why's he fidgeting like that? Why is he so restless - can he really be trusted to settle down and shut up? Maybe he's a claustrophobe who'll freak out in a minute and start shouting his head off?

What had seemed like a pleasant hour now begins to stretch endlessly ahead. You glance at your watch - ten minutes have passed. People are starting to look at one another in a worryingly tense way. They're all, obviously, thinking about what's going on.

If you're clever, you'll be thinking too. You've never met any of these people before, and you know nothing about them... so who's to say what strange motivations some of them might have? You know only too well, for example, that there are some nutjobs in life that just *have* to win. They always seem to think they're the ones that should come out on top, and there's nothing they'd like more than watching others lose. How happy they would be, boasting to their pals that they put one over a room full of mugs.

Or maybe someone's going to have a panic attack and will run out shrieking? Or who's to say there isn't one of those bullies here who simply wants to take his anger out on a few innocents, deliberately disappointing them when they've invested their time. Maybe he's planning on letting them get their hopes up for a bit - and then really hurting them?

You force yourself to think logically. If people are as clever as you, then you have to assume they'll each be coming to the same conclusions. Who's to say if everyone in the room is trustworthy? Each one of them represents an unknown factor... and every one of them will be just like you in knowing that a bird in the hand is worth two in the bush. The £5,000 is certain, the £10,000 is uncertain.

And if other people are as smart as you're being, they'll be working out that it actually pays to shout out. In fact, one of them might start shouting out pretty soon.

But you're smarter than any of them, aren't you?

You shout out.

Now, should you be disgusted with yourself for making this decision? Possibly... but what other conclusion should a clear-thinking and logical person come to? You're simply being game theoretic, seeing through to the big truth in life that everything is always about the tug of war between what's good for the group, the team, society as a whole - and what's good for the individual.

But it's possible you're still wondering about whether these little dramas can be represented in numerical form. How are people's choices given scores that can then be analysed?

And are there games that will show how this works without involving mind-bending mathematics?

Pete about to do 'the right thing'.

CHAPTER FIVE

WHAT KIND OF SCENARIOS ILLUSTRATE THE FUNDAMENTAL IDEAS OF GAME THEORY? AND DID ANY OF THEM SHOW THAT VON NEUMANN'S CONCLUSIONS MIGHT BE WRONG - AND THAT HUMANS COULD ACTUALLY COOPERATE WITH EACH OTHER IF THEY WEREN'T IN TOTAL OPPOSITION? IF SO, WHAT CAME NEXT?

There are a few, fairly nontechnical games that were to emerge after von Neumann's original proposals, but which illustrate the principles of what he meant. A couple of the more famous ones are the Ultimatum Game and the Dictator Game, and they're often used to explore how people are prepared to share things out.

Before describing how they work, however, maybe it would help if I painted a bit of background colour? So let's say there's someone called Pete who's part of a group of twenty or so people; possibly it's a work situation. Anyway, everyone there knows each other.

The boss has gathered them together and he now calls for silence.

'Thanks for coming, everyone. I wanted you all to know that we've been putting our heads together about the success we've been having recently, and we've decided to show our gratitude by awarding Pete £1,000!'

Everyone cheers... Pete's obviously a popular man. Then he points to to somebody standing next to Pete called Tom and he continues: 'Pete, everyone knows that Tom's been helping you and I guess you'll want to share some of it with him - but how much you let him have is up to you.'

What happens? Every eye in the room swivels to stare at Pete. You can hear a pin drop.

Pete looks round at the sea of faces waiting for him to speak and then quickly says: 'Thanks a lot... I'm going to give Tom half.' Everyone relaxes. Smiles all round; Pete's done the 'right thing'. His reputation as a fair and trustworthy person is intact.

But why was this so important? Why didn't he simply say he was going to keep all the money?

It's because we live in a world of constant interaction and trading, and the importance of projecting an image of ourselves as dependable, decent human beings is so central to our social standing that dividing things up generously is lodged deep in our neuropsychology.

Socially, Pete's behaved properly - and people will continue to see him in a good light. And anyway, being so even-handed hasn't really cost him much as he didn't know he was going to get the money until the moment before. So, his colleagues will think he's a good guy - and he's £500 better off anyway.

But stop. Run the situation again but this time with different rules. Now Pete's not standing with a lot of other people in a group. Instead, he's been rung up on the internal phone and asked to meet the boss alone in a room. This time, there's only the two of them and the dialogue now goes like this:

'Close the door, Pete. Now, in strictest confidence, we think you've been terrific recently and we've decided to give you a £1,000 bonus. But perhaps you could have a think about sharing some of it with Tom as I understand he's been a great support to you.'

Pete says: 'I see. Thank you. Off the record, though, how much do you want me to give him?'

'That's entirely up to you, Pete. You're the one who knows Tom best and how much he's been contributing. But one thing I can reassure you of, is that no one will *ever* know what proportion you decide on. Not me, not him. It'll always be a secret.'

What does Pete do now? When he leaves the room he considers the matter for a bit and then decides to give Tom £100. Why not? It's £100 Tom didn't have before. And as it turns out, when he tells him, Tom is delighted with his windfall and Pete's generosity.

But suppose the secret *does* come out? Arrgh. Suppose Tom discovers that Pete had originally been given £1,000 but only gave him a tenth of it. What would his reaction be now? Utter disgust most probably, because what had seemed like a nice gesture now looks like a cheap betrayal. And, if Tom tells other people the story, Pete's reputation is likely to be trashed.

These are understandable situations. Life is rarely straightforward. Reactions depend on actions, and any number of research studies show that our perception of fair division is hugely shaped by the circumstances that lead up to it. This is what psychologists call 'framing'.

An example of this would be to ask how Pete would have felt if he'd been given the £1,000 by someone who'd put it this way:

'Pete, I know you've been going through a rough time recently, and we wanted you to have some money to give you, well... a bit of a lift. Here's a cheque for £1,000. By the way, I know that Tom's been a support to you too, and you might consider letting him have some of it.'

Would he give him half now? My guess is not and, indeed, research suggests that people have a markedly reduced compulsion to share generously when they've in some way emotionally 'earned' their right to the money.

Or what about if Pete was handed the gift like this: 'Pete, I'm really grateful for all the hard work you've been putting in over the last few weeks and I simply wanted you to know how much it means to us. We'd like you to have this bonus of £1,000. By the way, I understand that Tom's occasionally been helping you out as well, so you might let him have some of it.' What then? When the thanks and praise have been so personal that Pete's plainly 'earned' the lion's share?

Game theorists love tracking scenarios like this, and measuring the degree to which the behaviour of *Homo economicus* is shaped by factors that aren't entirely rational, and yet are nevertheless perfectly understandable.

You're probably wondering what any of this has got to do with game theory? Surely these sorts of stories are simply observations of our social psychology? Of course this must be true… *but what is leading to that psychology?* What are the logical processes behind it? And how did all those memes about moral interaction come to us, and what were they based on?

Well, see what you think of the Ultimatum Game first. Maybe it'll go some way to answering a few of these points. It uses the same 'gift giving' scenario, but then goes further than these examples by exploring what happens to the principles of sharing when the situation is less open-ended.

Once again, Pete is given a lump of money and asked to split it with Tom. But, this time, there's a twist to the game. That's because if Tom considers he's not being treated fairly - humiliated by being offered too small a share - then not only can he refuse what he's being given but, by turning it down, he can make sure that *Pete gets nothing as well*. He now has the capacity to *punish* him. That's how the ultimatum works.

What happens? Fascinating. That's because research studies can now track people's reactions and actually measure mathematically the degree to which the lure of hard cash affects their view of their own sense of self-worth. And what it illustrates is that people will *reject* what they're offered if they think their share is too unreasonable or unfair - even if they could really do with the money. Research among students, for example, (when do students ever turn down free money?) shows that the great majority of people would rather not get anything if doing so means they can see the nasty, selfish person that's made the insulting offer suffer as well. Remarkable.

There's then a variant of the same idea that's also very revealing. This time the mechanism is called the Dictator Game, and it sets out to ask whether individuals would act completely selfishly if they had a free hand in dividing up the money. Or whether they'd display some Adam Smith-like principles: '... which interest him in the fortunes of others.'

In this game Pete (the Dictator) still has to share an amount of money with Tom. But this time, Tom has to accept what he's given and, unlike the Ultimatum Game, he *can't* then punish Pete in any way. Simple, huh? You'd think that Pete would keep everything now he's bulletproof. Yet study after study shows that the opposite is true. Yes, something like 40% of people will hog everything, but the average amount handed over - quite unnecessarily one might say - is around 20% of the money.

Once again, 'framing' shapes the results. If the players are unknown to each other and kept physically apart, then the retained proportion rises. The reverse is also true: familia rity breeds generosity because reputation comes into play.

And, if Tom should in any way 'earn' the right to increase his share - by taking a simple quiz, for example, or being told to run a couple of miles - then his percentage of the take tends to increase in line with how onerous the task had been.

So, if one takes the Ultimatum Game, what do you imagine is the level at which the inferior partner (the Tom character in these examples) starts to calm down? When does he think that getting hold of *something*, even if it's not half, overcomes his dislike of the person who's so grudgingly handing it out?

All the research seems to arrive at the same general conclusion, even though people have different perceptions. Taken overall, individual scores can be plotted on a graph, and the curve of it shows that anything under about 35% of the pot is routinely rejected... and anything that's over this is largely acceptable.

Aha. Isn't this the universal principle that's at work in every symbiosis - whether it's in the natural world or in our own?

The game theoretic conclusions seem to point in exactly the same direction. Symbiotic unions with unequal benefits may be everywhere in life - and the 'inferior' partners may not like it (no doubt there'd be just as much grumbling among people when they settle for 35% as there would be from mitochondria about having to share a eukaryotic cell with the nucleus) - but that doesn't stop them from *accepting the benefits that come with the deal.*

'The single most important idea in game theory is… always put yourself in the other player's position. The trick is not to ask yourself what you would do in their position but to ask what they would do… but people are often irrational in certain, often unpredictable ways.'
Edward Rosenthal, *The Complete Idiot's Guide to Game Theory*

We humans have the same origins and directional drives as everything else in life, so why shouldn't we act out the same processes that arrive at unbalanced arrangements? It's always been obvious that symbioses are very, very rarely 'balanced' when they're viewed externally. But so what? Surely, it's rather like Milo Minderbinder describing his fake 'syndicate' in *Catch 22* when he says that: '... everyone has a share'.

In this respect, it's worth repeating the evidence of the entire history of genetic evolution - that everything in life is either in competition to take energy from something else, or cooperating to try and overcome the forces of entropy by making 1+1=3 synergies.

Sometimes organisms simply have to accept that although their share of the gain is subordinate to their partners, it's worth it to them to accept the deal - and not to be envious of what the other party's ended up with..

What this might add up to, perhaps, is that instead of continuing to use the 1+1=3 analogy, I should perhaps start using the rather more generalised idea of 1+1 = 1.9 +1.1 instead. This 'a third ish' proportion seems to be something of a general prescription for acceptance. Anything less invites instability and potential retaliation - and resentment in us humans. And anything more is a deal, however grumpy it might leave one of the parties.

As an example of this there was an interesting recognition of a large-scale Ultimatum Game when the UK voted to leave the EU in 2016. What happened was that after the initial surprise had died down, the bureaucrats in Brussels let it be known that they'd be demanding £100 billion from Britain as a divorce settlement. Many newspaper articles followed the announcement by expressing outrage that ordinary UK citizens should be put in this kind of arm lock by an embittered partner.

The result? There was a significant swell of public opinion that the country should have a 'no deal' Brexit and simply walk away and hand the EU *nothing*. Faced with this threat, proper negotiations began, and any game theorist that was paying attention would doubtless have allowed themselves a secret smile when a settlement was agreed in the £35 to £38 billion range.

Perhaps the most exaggerated version of finding acceptable levels of sharing is seen in the way a country takes taxes from its people and provides services in return. The finances that lie behind the social contract in other words.

Does the same underlying principle work here as well? It would seem so, and the US economist, Arthur Laffer, famously illustrated this on a paper napkin while he was having lunch with the then Vice President, Dick Cheney.

Just as in fair division games, he explained, the two extremes of taxation were equally unacceptable. At one end of the spectrum, if no one was ever charged tax, then there'd be no money for social services. At the other end, if people were made to give up 100% of their earnings in tax, then they'd either leave the country or come up with a host of fiddles and stunts to avoid declaring their true income. But where should the tax policy fall between these two poles? What was 'fair'?

Of course, said Laffer as he drew the rough shape of a bell curve, nobody likes paying tax, but there's an underlying acceptance of the need to do it if people want to end up with a civilised country. The curve will change for different people, depending on their individual earnings, but the general principle is that any acceptance they may have for paying up diminishes as the rate rises until it reaches a 'saddle point', after which resentment, avoidance and corruption set in. This increases in line with the tax rate.

Now, Arthur Laffer has always been at pains to say that his drawing wasn't an original idea and that similar examples date back to Adam Smith and beyond.

Von Neumann's Minimax principle assumes the same shape. But the name stuck and the Laffer Curve has become one of the mainstays of modern macroeconomic policymaking.

And what do the endless studies show to be the saddle point for the overall, consolidated tax take that a democratic country can impose before further rises start to be counterproductive to continuing prosperity? Ha, 36%. Far left politicians may put their fingers in their ears and start humming 'nah, nah, nah' as they embark on impassioned demands for more taxation income from their successful corporations and high earners.

But the country as a whole, the organism, always seems to suffer if this goes on for long. Going much beyond an all-inclusive 'one third ish' split appears to lead to countries becoming unstable and unproductive. This finding increases in line with the overall take until one ends up with the deranged economies of places like Venezuela or Zimbabwe, where cooperation breaks down, and a collaborative culture is replaced by social injustice and rampant corruption.

Of course, what you've no doubt spotted is that all these games and economic examples involve some level of *communication* between the partners. Von Neumann's bleak Minimax conclusion may have shown that avoiding the worst was the best that we could hope for… but that was in non-cooperative, zero sum games of complete opposition.

Someone was now about to join the story who was going to investigate whether the same kind of outcomes arose if there were ever *non-zero* parts to the deal. His name was John Nash and he, too, had coincidentally come to Princeton and then astonished people with his prodigious talent.

Unlike von Neumann, though, he'd been born into a modest background in West Virginia, but he, too had rattled through his undergraduate degrees, completing them with brilliant grades by the time he was nineteen. When he decided on Princeton for his PhD, his professor famously wrote a reference letter with just the six words of commendation: 'This man', he said, 'is a mathematical genius.'

Nash went to New Jersey to study under the Canadian professor, Albert Tucker, and he soon became exposed to von Neumann's intriguing new thinking on game theory. Like many of Tucker's students, Nash's great brain fired up, and it wasn't long before he began to wonder whether it was possible, if the people in these games weren't locked into having just one way of playing, that they might use mixed strategies to find their best approach.

> '**The only kind of non-cooperative games von Neumann treated were two-person, zero sum games - which are necessarily non-cooperative. Nash's work was primarily concerned with non-zero sum games and games of three or more players.'**
> **William Poundstone, *The Prisoner's Dilemma***

As with so many of the new friends he'd made at the university, Nash probably found himself coming in at the start of a new week and spending a few minutes over a cup of coffee discussing the football games they'd seen over the weekend. Among the more irritating of the opinions he'd have heard would come from people who were known as 'Monday morning quarterbacks' - the sofa know-alls who'd slag off their team's tactics, and loudly tell everyone how they'd have played instead.

John Nash could see only too well that these touchline generals were speaking nonsense. No doubt he'd have kept his own counsel - but if the way a team chose to play became obvious on the pitch, why wouldn't the opposing team's quarterback simply change *his* game plan in response to what was happening?

Surely, like the small boys and their cake, each player would be making his decisions depending on how the other team was choosing to play? This would mean employing mixed strategies.

But what if one of the quarterbacks chose not to change, he asked himself? What if his tactics were fixed because he kept following his coach's instructions? More to the point, what happened in situations that weren't so black and white?

Ball games were bound to be zero sum because one side won and the other lost - but what about non-footballing situations where the outcomes weren't necessarily dependent on the strategies of implacable opponents? What if the interests of the parties weren't completely in opposition - what if they were non-zero ones, in other words? What would happen if one or other of them thought there might be synergies available if they worked together - and could guess at what the other person would be thinking?

As von Neumann had before him, Nash now brought his ferocious intellect to exploring the questions mathematically. If these were the circumstances, he argued with himself, and there was a degree of cooperation about making mutual gains - then shouldn't it be easier to come to rational solutions?

Russell Crowe as John Nash in *A Beautiful Mind*.
Nash himself is on the right.

He chose to explore these issues for his doctoral dissertation. It was submitted in 1951, after only two years' work... and it came to the *opposite* conclusion. In a staggeringly condensed series of mathematical proofs that ran to only twenty-eight pages, he answered the key question that participants in games like these should always put to themselves: 'If', he proposed they would ask, 'I know everyone else's strategy - and treat them as *fixed* - would I benefit or lose out if I switched my own approach?'

The results? At base, even though he'd introduced the possibility of non-zero collaboration, they were similar to John von Neumann's conclusions. There'd be a stalemate. But Nash's profound finding went further, and he said that if each player's strategy was optimal when set against the decisions of others... then it, too, would result in a dead end.

In this case it was to become recognised throughout the world as a 'Nash Equilibrium'.

> 'Poker is an example of 'I think he thinks that I think that he thinks that I think...'
> Such circular reasoning would seem to have no conclusion. Nash squared the circle
> by using a concept of equilibrium whereby each player picks his best response
> to what the others do. Players look for a set of choices such that each person's
> strategy is best for him when all others are playing their best strategies.'
> Sylvia Nasar, *A Beautiful Mind*

Sadly, as Ron Howard's movie of Sylvia Nasar's biography of Nash, *A Beautiful*

Mind, was so movingly to show, it was only a few years later that the poor man was to descend into a nightmarish paranoid schizophrenic illness that he was only to slowly emerge from thirty years later.

In the meantime, what had happened to his thesis?

It had become famous, frequently employed as the central tenet in bargaining strategy, something that was used by advisers and mathematicians the world over. From trade union negotiating to the arms race, company price setting to commodity auctions, Nash's logic directed how people should examine the dynamics of the threats and opportunities that arose in competitive situations.

And what became of John Nash himself? Forty-three years after his doctorate had first been submitted, many of them spent prowling the halls of Princeton in the dead of night, leaving abstruse formulae on blackboards, the forgotten man of American mathematics emerged, shyly blinking into the spotlight, to be awarded the 1994 Nobel Prize for Economics.

'By broadening the theory to include games that included a mix of cooperation and competition, Nash succeeded in opening the door to applications of game theory to economics, political science, sociology and, ultimately, evolutionary biology.'
Sylvia Nasar, *A Beautiful Mind*

But what did his Equilibrium actually mean? And why was it so important?

Again, like Minimax, it was disappointing. When two people, or even coalitions, were in competition, it said, a Nash Equilibrium would occur when the parties arrived at a point from which there was *no incentive to change their decisions*. It was an impasse. They could probably see that they'd be better off if they altered their approach - if they were more cooperative in other words - but they nevertheless wouldn't change their positions because they were fearful that the other party might then take advantage of them.

Ouch, ouch, ouch. But how true is this? Pretty true would seem to be the answer as one looks around in life, seeing this awful truth being acted out by people and organisations that are stuck where they are, unable or unwilling to hold out the prospect of collaboration. Each of them always knows that they could make gains, if only the other side would also agree to change… but they aren't going to risk taking the lead and holding out an olive branch to make this possible *in case they're then exploited.* Just how well do we all know this? And just how often have we been caught up in situations like these ourselves?

But amongst this game theoretic logic there are bound to still be questions nagging away about what it all implies. Yes, of course, when two people come to share things out, or try to make a deal with each other, then they'll probably behave rationally. And if they're logical they'll soon stop their bargaining because each side would rapidly realise there's no point in risking further initiatives. So, where's the profit in that?

A good question... but do these conclusions really stop with just a couple of opposing parties? Can the lessons be extended to larger numbers of people? To societies? Even to entire countries?

Well, oddly enough, that was exactly what was going to be tested next. And talk about a real-life situation - this one was going to decide the fate of the entire world.

What was it?

It was nothing less than the Cold War.

'I want the whole film to be like a poker game...'
Stanley Kubrick, director of *Dr Strangelove*

CHAPTER SIX

SO FAR, GAME THEORY JUST SEEMED TO BE REINFORCING EVERYONE'S MOST NEGATIVE, DOG-EAT-DOG VIEWS ABOUT HOW LIFE WORKED. NOW GAME THEORISTS WERE GOING TO FIND OUT THAT CONFLICT AND FEAR DIDNT HAVE TO BE THE ONLY APPROACHES.

Voted No 1 on the IGN video site, No 6 by readers of the *Guardian* and No 2 by a BBC poll, *Dr Strangelove. Or How I Learned to Stop Worrying and Love the Bomb* ranks high on pretty well everyone's list of great comedy movies.

It's often described as Stanley Kubrick's masterpiece - a 'hilarious' satire about how a rogue US Air Force general triggers an American thermonuclear attack on the Soviet Union because, in his unhinged imagination, the Russians are stealing his 'precious bodily fluids'.

But how funny was it really?

We humans have always dealt with our most terrifying fears by finding comedy in them, but there must have been many times in the early days of nuclear stockpiling when sleepless nights seemed more appropriate than laughter. The American authorities, of course, dismissed the film's premise as being completely implausible (until a Congressional enquiry found that some of the country's missile silos were being guarded by a solitary soldier with an outdated rifle) but the public thought they had every reason to be frightened.

This general view was heightened during the 1960s when it became ever more obvious that the future of the world was being reduced to a colossal game of global poker, only understood by a bunch of game theory boffins who spent their time trying to scoop the pot.

For anyone aged under about fifty, or who was unwell during that Double History class, here's a little background to the origins of the Cold War.

The US and the Soviet Union, of course, had been nominal allies in the desperate fight to defeat Nazism, but the two power blocs had then become frozen in an exact geopolitical version of a two-person, none-cooperative Nash Equilibrium almost from the moment that Germany had surrendered. This meant that the world's map had become divided by an 'Iron Curtain' that kept the two political ideologies apart, and both sides were riven by the same deep insecurities about just how far the other one would go to win the race for global domination.

The Communist leaders, and Stalin in particular, had become increasingly paranoid that their inferior nuclear capability was leaving them vulnerable to the untrustworthy Yankee capitalist pigs. Although they'd first exploded an atom bomb in August 1949, the Soviets had then fallen behind in the technology race and it wasn't until the end of 1955 that they achieved anything approaching parity.

It was at this point that they developed a thermonuclear hydrogen bomb, and from then on the number of warheads each side had, and their readiness to use them, became the pivot about which international policy making turned. The rest of the world had little to say in the matter, and most countries were simply left holding their breath and praying that the Cold War didn't suddenly turn hot.

As the plot's noose tightens in *Dr Strangelove* and the tension becomes almost unbearable, the President and his military advisors gather in an underground War Room, desperately trying to recall their bombers. But even among the angst and growing panic, they're also attempting to work out if they can use the situation to their advantage.

Kubrick's intentions for these scenes soon became apparent when he asked his Production Designer, Ken Adam, to build him a round table covered in green felt for the hawkish generals to sit at. Above it, he specified that a circular track of harsh lights should be suspended a few feet over their heads. The enigmantic Dr Strangelove, as ever, hovers close by in his wheelchair.

'I want the whole film to be like a poker game', Kubrick said, 'like the general staff and the President and everybody is playing a game of poker for the fate of the world.'

One by one the bombers respond to the coded messages they receive, ordering them to return to their bases. However, a single B-52, piloted by Major TJ 'King' Kong, can't be reached, and as they approach their target he gives the crew his down-home pep talk: 'Well, boys, Ah reckon this is it. New-q-lure combat, toe-to-toe with the Rooskies!'

With the bomb about to be dropped, the bluffing stage of the poker game comes to an end. It's time for each side to show their cards. And it's now that the Soviet Ambassador tells the President that their scientists have developed a Doomsday Machine that will 'trigger itself automatically' in the event of a nuclear attack. The retaliation it'll unleash, he says, will make the 'surface of the earth as dead as the moon.'

When he hears this Dr Strangelove realises that any game theoretic strategy is about to be as dead as they're all going to be. The US is about to 'get its hair mussed' and his voice rises to a shriek as he asks:

'The whole point of a Doomsday Machine is lost... if you keep it a secret! Why didn't you tell the world, eh?'

'It was to be announced at the Party Congress on Monday. As you know, the Premier loves surprises', the ambassador replies.

Yes, a satire of sorts. But, in reality, most people at the time were left wondering (and gibbering with fear) at what possible kind of idiotic logic could have lain behind the two countries' nuclear strategies. John von Neumann, however, would have been quick to argue that it was anything but idiotic.

In fact, he believed the policy made the greatest sense, even though he'd actually given it the most ironic term of all time... MAD. The acronym stood for Mutually Assured Destruction, and much as people might have disliked the idea, it worked. For a substantial part of the second half of the 20th century the knowledge that the two countries had weapons that would guarantee the annihilation of the entire planet was what kept the world at peace.

Since no one could win a war of this kind, went von Neumann's logic, he and the other military advisers believed there was a positive benefit to be had in balancing the thermonuclear capabilities of each side. True, neither of them might have any hope of victory, but because they also had no expectation of cooperation, then a stalemate would function. In a zero sum, non-cooperative game, he was to repeatedly say, minimising one's future risk was the maximum position that either party could aim for.

There hadn't always been this kind of equilibrium. In fact, it was fairly recent.

A few years earlier in 1948, the American Air Force, no doubt strongly influenced by von Neumann, had set up a workshop for superbrains called the Rand Corporation to 'think the unthinkable' about waging nuclear wars, the most likely of which would be against the Soviet Union.

Rand consultants hard at work. Critics said that the name stood for Research And No Development.

Rand was awarded a government contract and took offices in an anonymous building in Santa Monica with the objective of gathering in one place the most brilliant and inventive people in the country, and setting them the single-minded objective of *outthinking the Soviets*. From small beginnings it grew. Before long it had something like 500 full-time researchers, and around 300 carefully chosen consultants. Needless to say, von Neumann and Nash were among them.

What did it do? Much of its work went into simply understanding the enemy. Researchers spent hours poring over every aspect of Soviet existence, immersing themselves in the statistics of daily life there, and probing deeply into its culture, news and politics.

But the principal aim of the Rand consultants was to out-analyse the opposition. At base, they were war gaming. How should they respond to the other side's strategic initiatives and, in extremis, to a nuclear attack? How could they possibly win? And it was at Rand, perhaps more than at any university, that the elusive science of game theory was most closely explored and developed.

The folk singer, Pete Seeger came up with one of his famous songs about it:

> 'The Rand Corporation's the boon of the world
> They think all day long for a fee,
> They sit and play games about going up in flames,
> For counters they use you and me.'

'Think' they may have been doing, but in fact the MAD strategy wasn't adopted until quite late in the day. Before that, in the early 1950s, von Neumann's initial position had been, if anything, even more terrifying.

He and Bertrand Russell, the British mathematician (and pacifist!) were convinced that Stalin had inherited Hitler's bloodlust, and that war with the USSR would eventually prove to be inevitable. The two men joined forces to argue that the US should use its temporary advantage in nuclear capability to launch unprovoked attacks on Russian cities, and so gain a decisive supremacy.

The logic went that once they'd flattened the enemy - and brought Communism to an end - the US would then establish a world government. In short, they said, there was only room for one nuclear superpower - and that had to be the good guys. This was the only way to prevent another holocaust, and for the world's exhausted people to rebuild civilisation under a benevolent government.

The reasoning employed by the 'preventative war' brigade was irrefutable. Game theory had taught military strategists that if an enemy was so utterly committed to your destruction, and so completely cold-blooded and fanatical in its outlook, then there could only be one response. It was the Golden Balls logic writ large: in a finite, *one-time*, non-cooperative, zero sum, two person game there could only be one winner. And since that was the case, the winner had to be you.

For a time, America's foreign policy was hugely influenced by the game theoretic rationales of the 'first strikers'. Their opinions gained so much traction that, as von Neumann said in an interview with *Life* magazine (no doubt to send a message to the Soviets that America had adopted what they called the 'chicken' strategy): 'If you say why not bomb them tomorrow, I say, why not today? If you say today at five o'clock, I say, why not one o'clock?' It was pants wetting stuff.

But as the years passed and the USSR achieved nuclear parity, the Rand consultants changed their outlook. Now there could be no clear winner, they began to say, keeping the peace depended on symmetrical weaponry, and it was at this point that the MAD approach came into its own.

When there was no possible cooperation, and no 'end game', then the only strategy was to replace the imbalance with a hugely expensive arms race. This, the US hoped, would lead the Soviet Union to suffer such an economic nosebleed that the negotiating table - and an eventual climb down - might become preferable to the continued cost of preparing for conflict.

Not everyone at Rand was convinced that the MAD strategy should last forever. Back in 1950 a *Time* article had reported that: '... very few Americans now believe that the Kremlin can be conciliated or appeased with' and yet, as the following decade unfolded, and certainly after the death of Stalin, there were growing hopes that a measure of contact between the two countries might lead to low levels of cooperation and, from there to... well, who knew where?

Why weren't people happy to continue with the stability of MAD's Nash Equilibrium? It was because extreme hostility was almost certain to include a high level of risk. Geopolitics wasn't a one-time and unserious game like Golden Balls. Instead, it was a continuous series of shoves and pulls that were bound to lead to mistakes and possibly accidents. *Dr Strangelove* may have been an amusing piece of theatre, but its premise was only too scary: it didn't take much for minor cock-ups and miscalculations to bring the curtain down on the whole world. Unlike in the old days of military adventurism, zero sum warfare could become negative sum in the blink of an eye.

Both sides could lose.

Besides anything else, the Rand strategists could see that this kind of stand-off was getting in the way of the benefits of non-zero commercial activities. Pulling faces instead of growing customers was sucking energy out of the world's post-war recovery. John von Neumann was among those who were saying that a solution had to be found, even though it might not be ideal.

'Everybody was already bothered by the zero sum game. You're trying to decide whether to go to war or not. You couldn't say that the losses to the losers were gains to the winner. You did have cooperative game theory. But I couldn't force the other side to cooperate.'
Kenneth Arrow, *Rand consultant and 1972 Nobel Prize winner for Economics*

But how? How did one make an opponent cooperate if its leaders refused to? The world in general, and the US in particular, von Neumann said around this time: '... is riding a very fine tiger. Magnificent beast, superb claws, etc. But do we know how to dismount?'

How indeed? How could one side reach out a sharing hand to the other if actions like this were always going to be interpreted as a sign of weakness, veering away from collision in the world's game of chicken?

Well, the answer was going to be initiated by another of the astonishing Princeton

Merrill Flood and Melvin Dresher (right) about the time they realised that it can be rational to be irrational.

brainboxes. This was a Nebraskan named Merrill Flood who, after a brilliant contribution to wartime intelligence, was now consulting to Rand in a team with the Yale mathematician, Melvin Dresher.

They were working together on irrationality analysis when they dreamt up the most subtle and revealing of games… one, they thought, that could explore the interplay between zero sum and non-zero motivations in human exchanges in a way that had never been managed before.

They showed their idea to Nash's old tutor, Albert Tucker, who immediately saw its significance and quickly formalised it into the game-theoretic scenario that's become famous the world over. Tucker was due to give a speech at Stanford University in a few days' time, and he wanted to introduce the game there. To do this he added a formal mathematical structure to its outcomes, and then gave it the name that's launched countless PhDs, untold arguments, and a million sighs of irritation.

He called it The Prisoner's Dilemma.

But why the sighs of irritation? It's because it's almost impossible when one first hears about it not to groan at how silly the idea is, and then to give a further grunt at how obvious the answer has to be. But when most people are left for a few moments longer, second thoughts arise that generally lead to a more measured reaction of: 'ah, I see, not so easy'. And, from that point on, as vast numbers in the game theory village have found, it's difficult not to become lost in its revealing charms.

The result has been to make the scenario the window through which people have come to see the way that universal laws govern the conflict between individual and group interests.

And, it's not only human activity that it exposes. Over time, biologists and evolutionary theorists realised that they, too, could use its implications to see how organisms in the natural world take up their positions on the Behavioural Spectrum. By using the insights that flow from it, they've come to increasingly understand how and why everything interacts with the other life forms around them. Once the significance of these actions were seen, geneticists found that at last, they could answer the Guru's question of why *nothing ever wins over evolutionary time*... however successful the organism might appear to have been.

So, what was it? What was the game? Well, brace yourself for sighing. It goes like this...

Imagine there's been a major robbery at a remote country house one evening and the police have been called. They organise a search, and some time later, two thieves are picked up on the platform of a local railway station. There's no sign of the loot. The pair are brought to a nearby police station where they're put into solitary confinement - in separate cells, some distance apart so they can't see or hear each other.

The chief detective then visits them in turn. And he says exactly the same thing to each of them:

'Listen, we know all about you. I've looked up your records and you're plainly a couple of professionals who've been at it for years. Now, we can't find the stolen goods, no doubt you've got the stuff buried somewhere. And, actually, I've only got circumstantial evidence to convict you of the break-in. So, I'm going to need your help... I'm going to ask you to confess.

'So, here's the deal. If you both admit to the robbery and plead Guilty, then I'll see the judge goes easy on you when it comes to your sentence. Far less jail time than you'd get if we eventually nail you.

'But if you both stay schtum and don't admit to anything, then there's not much we can do. All right, I'll see you get done for trespass - we'll cook up some evidence for that - and you'll probably get a light sentence. Maybe a short spell in jail.

'OK, but listen very carefully now. If you confess you *did* do the job, but your mate stays silent - then we'll throw the book at him. I'll see he gets a life sentence...

and you'll walk free for turning state's evidence. Sure, you may feel bad about it later, but he's down for twenty years and you're in the pub. I'm going off duty now, but I'll come back and see you tomorrow morning at nine and I'll hear your answer then.'

This is no doubt the point at which you're looking baffled and asking what on earth any of this has to do with understanding how we humans work, never mind evolution. But stay with me and play the game. All right, if I have to, you say, then... 'very well, they'd both stay silent. That way the police can't lay a glove on them. There'll be some short jail time for the trumped-up charge of trespassing, but surely that's just an occupational hazard of being in the robbery business?'

However, it's a long night's wait. Now put yourself in the place of the prisoners. The blackness of the tiny cell undermines your confidence. The prospect of twenty years of this is just too awful to contemplate. Then comes the next thought. Can you *really* trust your partner? Won't the temptation of going free simply be too great for him to resist? If he was to shop you... you're inside forever. You'll be an old man when you get out, and he's been back home with his feet up all that time.

On the other hand, if you confess - and he doesn't - then *you'll* go free. And if he's thinking in the same way as you, and you both confess? Then you'll be rewarded by getting a lenient sentence anyway. The cop promised that.

The detective comes back the next morning and visits each of them in turn. He knows what to expect - he's been at this game a long time. They both confess.

Now, you're asking, isn't this just another parable? Another version of cold-hearted opposition? In a one-time game like this, the principle of von Neumann's Minimax has to hold good: however much you might want to cooperate, you daren't take a risk if you can't trust the other person to cooperate as well. Seems simple?

And yet, as Stephen Pinker was to describe in *The Better Angels of Our Nature:* 'The prisoner's dilemma has been called one of the great ideas of the 20th century, because it distils the tragedy of social life into such a succinct formula.'

Jean Jacques Rousseau had famously come up with much the same kind of insight a couple of hundred years earlier. He described how a group of villagers find a sleeping stag and form a tight circle to surround it. They walk slowly inwards with their knives out, knowing that if they all hold firm the poor thing will have no escape. And what a prize it is... something that would feed everyone in the village for days.

But just as the animal jerks awake and realises it's being trapped, one of the men sees a rabbit hopping around, and he leaves the circle to grab it. The stag immediately charges through the gap and is away before anyone can fill it.

Rousseau used the story to illustrate the hopelessness of us ever expecting social responsibilities to override our personal greed. His logic was that the stag might have got through anyway, while the rabbit was a certain catch. And the rabbit would feed the man's family... that was his individual responsibility, not the one he owed the village. Sure, the others in the circle would think he'd let them down, but come on, he's got himself to think about.

It was the social dilemma in a nutshell.

What's the difference between this and the prisoners' thought processes? Not much, you'd probably say. Looking after number one, and letting the others go hang seems to be the lesson of life.

But is that right? If we all followed that logic then there'd never be such a thing as a fair, moral or effective society. Yet we've clearly evolved to create them, and they're plainly the cornerstone of our existence. What, then, was the process that led to their stability?

It was at this point that another of von Neumann's great innovations came into its own... computers. These hadn't been around when the old sages like Rousseau and Hume were using stories and parables to illustrate how life worked. But the early calculating machines were now available, and it wasn't long before the academics and game theorists at Rand began to realise they could be programmed to see which decisions would win over the long term - *in multiple plays rather than just in one-offs.*

If the game wasn't seen as an abyss into which one could fall, so much as an opportunity to learn something about the people one was playing, would an *iterated* prisoner's dilemma (known technically as an IPD) throw up different results? If decision-making situations were repeated, would the parties alter their behaviour and attempt to get some benefits, rather than just being stuck in an equilibrium of suspicion and conflict?

In other words, the boffins began looking to see if *cooperation could evolve.*

What Albert Tucker did now was to give the possible outcomes of the prisoner's dilemma a series of scores. By doing this, he figured, computer simulations might become possible.

First, he said, let's say a confession, and the other man staying silent, wins 5 points. Then the poor fellow that's on the wrong end of this defection should get none - hardly surprising as he's in clink for twenty years. No points for him. (By the way, in the language of game theory this is known as the 'sucker's payoff'. Not very nice is it?)

Then if *both* men confess, say each of them gets 1 point. This is better than none as they'll have been given lighter sentences, even though they're still doing prison time.

And if they each stay silent and simply get done for trespass? Then they score 3 points each. Why 3? Because the halfway point between 5 for winning and 0 for losing is 2.5. Yet staying silent is an example of being cooperative. In this case, the thieves should be rewarded in a way that shows there's been a *gain* between them.

So, the scoring possibilities that the game theorists all agreed reflected the possible decisions came out at 0, 1, 3 and 5. That seemed about right. The balance between the zero sum outcome of someone winning at the expense of someone else losing, would be outweighed by the gains that the pair could make if they cooperated.

Two lots of 3 points made 6. That was better than 5 and 0… it was the 1+1=3 principle in action. Non-zero gains were being dangled in front of the thieves' noses, *if they could only find a way of overcoming the trust barrier.*

Flood and Dresher's early work with Tucker's scoring was intriguing. They realised, of course, that always playing 'Defect' (confessing) had to be rational, and it became known as the *dominant* strategy. It was called that as it was the logical thing to do… because one would win if the other person played Cooperate (and stayed silent), but one could still be certain of getting a single point if the other man also chose to defect.

> **"Tis better to have loved and lost than never to have loved at all.'**
> **In other words, love is a dominant strategy.'**
> **Avinash Dixit and Barry Nalebuff, *Thinking Strategically***

What these 'Defect' people never left themselves exposed to was being the sucker, and therefore getting nothing. This approach - what game theorists took to calling 'Always Defect' - had to be the way that a logical, amoral person would play if he was completely set on beating the other man. Repetition didn't come into it. It didn't matter if the game was played a thousand times, the unemotional competitor would see each one of the series as a separate one-time game.

Why would a rational person change his strategy?

This was exactly what was happening on the geopolitical stage. The computer simulations of the two person, non-cooperative, zero sum games were showing exact parallels with the US and USSR stand-off. It was nothing less than a repeated Nash Equilibrium in which both sides could logically see that they'd be better off if they ever cooperated - but neither would take the risk of trying to do so.

Now the Rand mathematicians began to wonder what would happen if a player tried to break the deadlock? What would the outcome be if one of the opponents played Cooperate - holding out an olive branch to see if he couldn't entice the other person into sharing six points? If this happened and the players found they liked the gains, and in time they learnt to trust each other, then a pattern of playing 'Always Cooperate' would take hold and the two sides could settle down into an easy life of long-term collaboration. Not necessarily friendship, but a 'rational' peace.

The answer, sadly, was that the Cooperate gambit was doomed to failure because the dominant strategy of defecting simply took advantage of an approach from a naive, trusting opponent.

If one was set on choosing the dominant strategy of Defect all the time, and the other suddenly played Cooperate, then five points would come their way and the other person would get the black eye of no score.

Think on though. Was this really such a clever thing to do?

Of course, under the terms of the game the constant defector - someone who chose Defect every time the game was played - might have a uniformly hostile and competitive approach, but there could be a price to pay for it. Who, in real life, wants to deal with someone who is flatly, endlessly difficult, only ever thinking about themselves and resistant to the gains that can come from being collaborative? If you tried to get on with a person like this, you'd soon become frustrated at always coming up against a brick wall.

Yes, the Rand researchers were saying, this choice might win the battles, but it would surely lose the war. If someone constantly played like this, then his *reputation* would suffer. People would see him as an intransigent, impossible person and, ultimately, very few people would ever want to deal with him.

In fact, most normal people would *avoid* him. Why's that? It's because it was just like the rationale for trading relationships… who would ever want to deal with someone who was always determined to beat you? OK, the other party might argue that he was protecting himself as an individual, but society as a whole wouldn't want him to be a part of it.

But was the premise of the prisoner's dilemma a realistic scenario anyway? After all, we rarely deal with people with whom we have *no* knowledge, even if the information we have about them, and their motives, is imperfect. What if the two men in their cells had known each other? The heart of the Dilemma lay in them only having a binary choice in that they'd either trust the other person, or they didn't. It was from this that they'd make their decision about whether to cooperate or defect.

The idea behind the game was to see what players did when they were in blind opposition. But in reality, people tend to have a pretty good idea about how another person is likely to react. Even if we don't know them well, we're instinctively picking up a blizzard of unknown and unseen messages that the other person is giving off. And we've become super sensitive over evolutionary time when it comes to judging how people are likely to behave.

This is exactly how a good poker player operates. He decides on what an opponent has got in his hand by relying on his knowledge of the cards on view - but also on his intuition about the other players' probable behaviour. In the same way, the opponents in the Cold War weren't completely in the dark about each other.

Quite the opposite, in fact, their information might have been imperfect, but they'd both grown in confidence over time that they could fairly accurately predict how the other would react.

Flood and Dresher realised this and now set out to run some lab experiments with players who weren't complete strangers. What would happen, they wanted to know, when people were given the task of 'winning' by getting the highest score?

The pair approached a couple of the other Rand consultants, Armen Alchian and John Williams, and asked them if they'd play the prisoner's dilemma over a series of a hundred separate games. What they were looking for was to see if patterns of behaviour developed. They therefore replicated the police station conditions, and kept the two men apart and unable to communicate.

The pair were then asked to simultaneously write down, for each game, a 'C' if they wanted to Cooperate (by staying silent) or 'D' if they chose to play Defect... in other words, to confess to the crime. At the end of each game, the men were told what the other had selected. In this way, they had the chance to 'learn' from the other one's choices.

So, what strategy ended up with the most points? Surely it was the one that got the most 1 scores, and even the occasional 5 that would come from endlessly refusing to trust the other side?

No, actually that strategy didn't win at all... in fact, the results weren't what one would have expected. Surprisingly enough, mutual defection - the most obvious and logical outcome - only occurred in fourteen of the hundred games. The Nash Equilibrium should by rights have been happening more frequently, if not constantly... and yet it wasn't. Instead, either Alchian or Williams tended to play 'Cooperate'.

'The prisoner's dilemma shows us that all life is about pushing forward to trust - because we all know the benefits of being able to trust people - and yet being able to defend oneself if they let you down...trust is the very foundation of social and economic life. But is it irrational? Do we have to override our instincts to be nice to each other?'
Matt Ridley, *The Origins of Virtue*

When the two of them were asked about it later, both reported that the lure of the joint gains that could come from choosing to 'Cooperate', and each getting three points, was *strong enough to overcome their doubts*. But if they did, and their 'gambit' was refused - and the other person played 'Defect' - then they'd immediately revert to defecting.

Put simply, there was an element of reaching out, but if this wasn't met with cooperation in return, then they both immediately chose to 'punish' the other person by then defecting themselves.

Hmm. What was happening?

First, it was apparent that if there was a degree of continuous meetings between people, then clearly the zero sum outcome of a single game was less likely to happen. As Matt Ridley was to explain in his great book, *The Origins of Virtue*: 'Selfishness was not the rational thing to do after all - as long as the game is played more than once.'

Secondly, it was also plain that however much one might have imagined that these games would be played by cold blooded opponents, quickly reaching the logical conclusion that it was rational to defect, the same deep instinct for 1+1=3 that's seen everywhere in the natural world made them find it actually *more rational* to try and make cooperative gains.

This is, perhaps, one of the great insights of the human species. *It's rational to be irrational*. Our genetic and biological drives might have made us recognise that we can either win by beating others, or succeed by helping everyone win, but it's quite evident that our reasoning apparatus has also come to exactly the same conclusion.

We're capable of seeing through the shortcomings of getting stuck in a game theoretic equilibrium. Ken Binmore explains this in his book, *Game Theory*: 'If the great game of life played by the human species were adequately modelled by the prisoner's dilemma, we wouldn't have evolved as social animals! Rational players don't cooperate in the prisoner's dilemma because the conditions necessary for rational cooperation are absent.'

But, thirdly, it wasn't just the repeated nature of the games that was behind the result... and this became clear towards the end of the series. It was logical, both Alchian and Williams said, to defect on the 100th game, because this was an opportunity to grab a final five points if the other person was playing 'C', to cooperate. Why's that? It was because the other person wouldn't then be able to punish them for their choice. Since there was no 101st turn, they couldn't play 'Defect' back.

However, because this was an outcome that would be obvious to both players, what came to be known as a 'backward induction paradox' emerged in which the realisation was bound to lead to a defection on the 99th turn.

And, since this was equally logical, then there had to be a similarly rational decision to play 'Defect' on the 98th... and so on, and so on. Back and back they would go under this reasoning. Yes, they might both want cooperation - but, how could you trust the other side not to start this tactic early?

The lesson was plain. If you want to maintain cooperative relationships, you should get to know somebody well, and then deal with the same person over long periods of time. Stick to dealing with people whose behaviour you could pretty well predict was the message. And as far as possible, avoid one-time games, and the kind of cliff edge situations you get when iterated relationships come to an end.

What was also clear was that although it had initially seemed rational to play Defect, it now appeared even more logical to Cooperate.

The structure of the prisoner's dilemma was time limited with one-offs like Golden Balls, and it's true that there's no reasonable alternative but to defect in these cliff-edge situations, particularly if you're never going to see the people again. But when the game is played repeatedly, then it's plainly attractive to look for the gains that can come from collaboration.

But how do you get someone to cooperate with you?

What an insulting question, eh? Surely it's because you're a good chap, a trustworthy person. Everyone knows that. But are you really always being trustworthy? Or are you sometimes putting your cooperative arm around someone's shoulders - only to stab them in the back?

It's certainly nice to grab 5 points every now and then, isn't it? And are you really sincere about being trustworthy, or are you bluffing... and is the person you're dealing with doing the same thing back to you?

Well, if you want to know why people would deal with you, it has to be because you've built a *reputation* for being sincere. This means you'll do what you say you will, you'll always be trustworthy and, as far as possible, you will stick to dealing with people who've also proved themselves to be trustworthy. I guess this would have been the kind of behaviour that Adam Smith would have deemed as 'lovely'.

It's therefore hardly surprising that as humans evolved, we've become superb at sending out these sorts of messages about ourselves. And we're also superb at being able to read the signs in others, seeing through the bluster and ambiguities, and working out what suits us. And we've learnt how to carry out this process instinctively, intuitively and at lightning speed, endlessly weighing up people's responses, and looking at their reputational record, defecting and cooperating with a huge range of people as easily as we carry out any other function.

> '... human behaviour is mainly the result of social
> norms and rarely the result of considered decisions...'
> Peter Richerson, *Not By Genes Alone*

Not really head shaking stuff, you're no doubt thinking, but as Edward Rosenthal was to say in his entertaining book *The Complete Idiot's Guide to Game Theory*: 'When games are played repeatedly, the strategies that people employ are, in a very real sense, *more* rational than the theory prescribes. This super rationality manifests itself in people's surprising tendency to cooperate with others. The evidence is that we're rational to some extent, but when… we deviate from cold blooded mathematical computation… we're not only understandable, but fairly systematic.'

Systematic? What could that mean? Was there a right and wrong way to do things?

Well, now researchers were going to use the prisoner's dilemma to lift the bonnet of our social symbioses… and to try and find out how the engine worked.

Symmetries of Games

An automorphism, or symmetry, of a game will be a permutation of its pure strategies which satisfies certain conditions, given below.

If two strategies belong to a single player they must go into two strategies belonging to a single player. Thus if ϕ is the permutation of the pure strategies it induces a permutation ψ of the players.

Each n-tuple of pure strategies is therefore permuted into another n-tuple of pure strategies. We may call χ the induced permutation of these n-tuples. Let ξ denote an n-tuple of pure strategies and $P_i(\xi)$ the pay-off to player i when the n-tuple ξ is employed. We require that if

$$j = i^\psi \qquad \text{then} \qquad P_j(\xi^\chi) = P_i(\xi)$$

which completes the definition of a symmetry.

The permutation ϕ has a unique linear extension to the mixed strategies. If

$$s_i = \sum_\alpha c_{i\alpha} \pi_{i\alpha} \qquad \text{we define} \qquad (s_i)^\phi = \sum_\alpha c_{i\alpha} (\pi_{i\alpha})^\phi .$$

The extension of ϕ to the mixed strategies clearly generates an extension of χ to the n-tuples of mixed strategies. We shall also denote this by χ .

We define a symmetric n-tuple $\mathcal{A}$ of a game by

$$\mathcal{A}^\chi = \mathcal{A} \qquad \text{for all} \quad \chi\text{'s}$$

it being understood that χ means a permutation derived from a symmetry ϕ .

A page from John Nash's original PhD thesis. Game theory's origins may have involved ferociously complicated mathematics, but the insights were remarkable.

CHAPTER SEVEN

FROM THE EARLY 1950s ONWARDS, GAME THEORISTS WERE BECOMING INCREASINGLY CONVINCED THAT IF THEY COULD ONLY GET THE VARIABLES RIGHT, THE ITERATED PRISONER'S DILEMMA WOULD DRAW THE CURTAINS APART AND SHOW HOW HUMANS DECIDED ON THEIR BEHAVIOUR. BUT DID THEIR COMPUTER SIMULATIONS REALLY MAKE ANY PROGRESS? AND IF SO, WHAT DID THEY FIND?

Once they had their hands on it, the massed battalions of the world's social scientists and evolutionary theorists descended on the intricacies of the prisoner's dilemma with all the expectations of the ancients consulting the Delphic oracle. Surely, many of them felt, if they could only find the magic alloy of outcomes, utilities and timeframes, then they'd squeeze a set of universal rules about how to 'win' in life from the various decision trees and choice matrices.

It had to be possible, some were now convincing themselves, that if they applied enough brainpower to modelling the risks and rewards of how cooperation, self-interest, gains and punishments interacted, a Golden Age would be unveiled in which they'd come up with a general prescription for our ideal behavioural choices.

In particular, a host of different academic disciplines now convinced themselves that they could use the Dilemma's mechanisms to find solutions to the most fugitive of their problems. A friend of mine who studied at Stanford for an MBA in the early 1970s, for example, still tenses into a rictus of anxiety at the memory of his 'decision analysis' courses in competitive pricing policies and bargaining strategies.

But what are we amateurs and non-mathematicians to make of it all? Did interrogating the prisoner's dilemma really lead to anything useful? Well, actually yes, it did. Quite a lot, in fact. But while many of the findings seemed to be more of the 'bleeding obvious' kind than jaw-slackening surprises, the fact that behavioural conclusions could now be supported by hard mathematical logic were making people think there had to be merit in using the Dilemma to tackle some of our thorniest social issues.

First, though, it was rapidly becoming apparent that when humans were being used as lab rats, the Alchian-Williams results weren't outlying oddities at all. Instead, their results were usually being replicated whenever the research was repeated. What was plain was that the search for cooperation was far more instinctively desired than people had thought.

Then, secondly, it was ever more evident that if respondents were informed about the other person's choice at the end of each game, then there didn't seem to be much merit in having them make their choices either simultaneously or covertly.

Researchers were now seeing that simultaneous decision-making - arrived at without a strategy - could lead to the kinds of shortcomings one gets in the Rock, Paper, Scissors game. And as anyone who's ever played it knows, it's almost impossible to judge if your opponent is employing a reasoned approach, or simply choosing 'random' each time. It's also impossible to punish someone for making a decision that doesn't suit you.

Nonetheless, if one watches people as they play the game, silly and unpredictable though it is, it's an insight into how we try and forecast what others are going to do. Take a careful look at the players and you'll see them intently scanning each other's faces for the kind of hints and 'tells' that poker players use to predict their opponents' thoughts. But guessing on this basis can be thin gruel. Although it might look like a behavioural game, even long-run, iterated versions of it show that any attempt to predict an opponent's strategy is more likely to leave people frustrated than informed.

To avoid this limitation, game theorists now switched their focus away from simultaneous choices, and towards *sequential* ones. They also stopped having people in separate rooms and using codes for their choices. Better by far, researchers found, were the results that arose when people could take a good look at their opponent and come to conclusions about their likely behaviour.

By making these changes they took contestants away from the pretend drama of Rock, Paper, Scissors, and nearer to acting out how we actually behave in the marketplace of real life. Why's that? It's because everything, from mutational evolution to poker bids, conflict situations like the small boys' cake cutting and on to negotiating tactics, all show that knowing the decision of the *other person* is the key to deciding how we should then play ourselves.

What the Dilemma had illuminated was that if the interests of the players were completely opposed, then whatever the other person might decide to play, the only rational choice in simultaneous play was to Defect. But now, sequential choices meant that if someone could see whether the other player was sticking with the dominant, 'safe' strategy of defection... or whether he was asking for cooperation, then they'd make better decisions. If you knew the other's choice, you'd know how to respond - either by matching the defection or by joining in with someone's wish to collaborate. If they played Cooperate then you could respond with this yourself - and you'd get your share of the six point reward that's on offer when people work together.

Playing sequentially emphasised how important it was to *learn* about the person you were dealing with as you went along. Instead of being in the dark about your opponent's strategy, his motives would become clearer over time, and you'd now be able to assess his position before you had to make your own move. As, indeed, the other person could as well when he was deciding how to deal with you.

The next thing that became pretty apparent was that twiddling the dials of outcome variables and utility values would hugely influence the results. The original prisoner's dilemma format had been written in a deliberately extreme way to highlight the available decisions.

But the choices one faced in life were rarely as exaggerated as these. The 'sucker's' punishment in the way the Dilemma was framed, for example, was terrifyingly severe. Similarly, the freedom prize was arguably too enticing to resist. And the cliff edge timeframe meant that no one but the boldest of players would ever think that trying to cooperate under these circumstances was worth it.

Even though one's life choices might follow the same logic of zero sum and non-zero decisions that the Dilemma was throwing up, what the researchers were now saying was that the stakes are seldom so sharply defined, nor the punishments as harsh, as they're described in the game.

In the same way, it's very unusual when dealing with people that one's as totally devoid of information about another person's reputation as the Dilemma describes. It's implausible that you'd ever be completely in the dark about how others are likely to behave. Conversely, the more you know about them (and the more you've seen of how they've responded in previous situations) the more possible it is to weigh up the likelihood of how they'll act under different circumstances.

So, where was this all going?

Social scientists began to look for more clues as they pursued further rounds of trials. New generations of test subjects were now being chosen who *knew* one another before they were being asked to play. They could therefore be expected to guess whether their opponents were likely to be cooperators or defectors - and if they were the sorts of people who'd keep up this pattern of choice-making in the future. Researchers added this to their realisation that richer insights emerged when the games were played *openly*, with the contestants seeing what the other person was doing, rather than having the opponents or their choices being in any way hidden.

Intriguing results began to come through. When contestants kept meeting the same person and were having the opportunity to reward or punish them, it was becoming ever clearer that they would quickly see what the potential was for *dealing* with them. This was because players instinctively understood how to interpret the history of their interactions.

The Dilemma had begun as a high stakes conflict between cold-hearted opponents, but now the test subjects were being asked to sum each other up in the same way that they would in a poker game. And very quickly, people showed they could make good guesses about one another's strengths and weaknesses. Significantly, they were also showing themselves to be less worried about winning each individual hand, and much more focussed on what the *joint outcome* might be over the long run.

As the behaviour patterns of the test subjects would settle, it became increasingly apparent that the mathematical outcomes of the IPD were illustrating the same mechanisms Adam Smith had described as our natural human desire to 'truck, barter and exchange'. It was plain that this was a universal law that had emerged as we'd developed as a species.

But why was that? Well, researchers now began to speculate that once we'd taken the scale of our communities beyond the Dunbar Limit, then the success of trading, and of dividing our talents, skills and goods with non-family members, even strangers, had driven up human complexity. The formation of the resulting social symbioses had so wildly accelerated our development that we'd managed in a few hundred generations what mutational evolution had taken other species to achieve in millions.

Adam Smith's reasoning had seen through to this truth. He'd come to the conclusion by realising that an individual has to satisfy the needs of *other* people to get the benefits that he desires for himself. While this might mean he was acting out of self-interest, a person was nonetheless using the great trick of working efficiently with others to achieve the gains that he wanted.

Now game theorists were seeing the same thing. Although defection might be the rational choice, and understandably the dominant strategy… cooperation was what led to repeated opportunities. This was why one would patiently persist with someone, rather than ditching him as not worth the effort. Was this so surprising, though? Probably not.

Mankind's history has always shown how the process worked: how cooperation had evolved with the benefits of speech and written communication, how its growth was accelerated by the division of labour, and how it had then been supercharged by the mutual gains that came from the widespread trading of people's skills and goods.

Ultimately, this had led to it becoming lodged deep in our instinctive behaviour by the rewards that arose from specialisation and exchange. It's therefore unsurprising that these were precisely the mechanisms that we chose to build our large societies on.

> 'The life of each individual is so conditioned by the life of others that it
> would be impossible, even assuming it were convenient to do so, to isolate oneself
> and live one's own life - social solidarity is a fact, from which no one can escape.'
> Errico Malatesta, *Life and Ideas*

The entire process of living our lives through collaborating with others has been going on for so long, and has become so central to our natures, that game theorists now began seeing the Dilemma as highlighting a moral choice. Acting cooperatively, they were now concluding, was the *right thing to do*, while defecting from other people appeared selfish and antisocial. In fact, this has been so evident in the direction of human cultural evolution that many of our memes now demonise self-serving behaviour, and praise selflessness and sacrifice. One might almost say that social deviations, sin and even evil, are simply descriptions of people giving free rein to their selfish drives.

The moral lesson of the Dilemma was that humans are endlessly reaching out for cooperation. And yet, and yet… everybody also knows that people can make zero sum choices just as quickly and as effortlessly as they can non-zero. But why would we ever do that when it's clear that being cooperative is a winning strategy?

Well, it's obvious that we choose to play the zero sum 'Defect' strategy either to punish people who do it to us… or to gain a sudden advantage over someone who's cooperating. After all, which of us is without sin? As Albert Einstein used to say: 'It is easier to denature plutonium than to denature the evil from the spirit of man.'

And it's also plain that this instinct stems from our genetic heritage - it's where we've come from. We didn't spring fully formed as human beings. Instead we've evolved from non-sentient life forms that had been succeeding by playing both strategies over billions of years. *Homo sapiens* took on this inheritance, and then adapted it within the giant changes that arose with of our cultural evolution.

The result is that we've now arrived at our ethical framework - and also our ability to get an advantage by taking more than we're giving. Yes, the origins of our behavioural choices may remain profoundly genetic but, to quote Richard Dawkins yet again, we have evolved '... to the point where we are capable of overcoming our selfish genes.'

'On the whole, human beings want to be
good, but not too good, and not all of the time.'
George Orwell, *All Art Is Propaganda*

The moral reasoning that game theory has come to expose is best seen in how it shows up in that byword for cronism and corruption: the capitalist system. That's because bad people can always be expected to cheat the unwary, and unless this is resisted, it can lead to worrying inequalities. Nevertheless, capitalism also brings with it huge benefits to the pacification process of human behaviour, in that it shines a light on how we interact, and shows up who is going to help us, and who isn't.

This tension was highlighted by the Harvard anthropologist, Joseph Heinrich, in his book *The Secret of Our Success*. In it he wrote about the way: 'In a system of free exchange, individuals succeed not by favouring kin over strangers, but by cultivating a reputation for impartial fairness and cooperation, because these qualities will help them attract customers and the best business partners.'

'Our freedom of choice in a competitive society rests on the fact
that, if one person refuses to satisfy our wishes, we can turn to another.'
Friedrich Hayek, *The Road to Serfdom*

Put at its simplest, the approach is nothing less than our version of the Horizontal Gene Transfer process that made bacterial life so successful. Our choices are all part of the endless shifting of strategies we make as we deal with the people around us. As we do this, we show ourselves to be protean beings: multifaceted, making our decisions in a flash, sometimes being sincere, sometimes mendacious, sometimes bluffing and sometimes anxious to be believed. But, always, always, always... we're looking to *win*. Is it too cynical to find ourselves agreeing with WH Auden when he wrote: 'You shall love your crooked neighbour, With all your crooked heart'?

It's at this stage that the gentler souls among us will recoil and murmur that they feel no need to win, no compulsion to beat their fellow man. 'I'm not even competitive!' they'll insist. Many of us may indeed truly feel this, but deep within us there's a different tale. Whether we like it or not, every one of us has the same ticking genetic imperative to succeed, to keep going, to stay alive and to reproduce… because, if you don't, then mankind will soon be joining the 99.9% of species that are no longer with us.

We know this has to be the case, even if it's only as a vague inconvenience to our sense of self-regard. But game theory has come along to show us that we're constantly deciding on what suits us best, and as we do this, we're acting on the same directional drives that makes every other thing in life try to deal with what's around it. The story is always the same: grab energy to survive, and then search for the mutual gains available from dealing with other organisms to ward off entropy. Conflict and cooperation.

Game theorists were by now coming to the conclusion that when the prisoner's dilemma was played over long periods of time, the outcomes were showing how the reputational element of repeated cooperation was dependent on *trust*… on trusting the other person not to suddenly pull out a defection and therefore to betray one's attempts to cooperate. Why would people ever do this though? Well, it's because there's the ever-present temptation to grab a five point victory when the other person is trying to install a long-run fair division. This leads to the sad truth that the more we trust, the more we invite dodgy people to snatch at an easy advantage.

But there's a price to be paid if they do this. And that's because getting a cheap gain from a trusting partner might bring a short-term lift, but it can paradoxically lead to a far higher level of damage than if the person hadn't been trusted in the first place.

Why's that? Well, think about how you'd feel if you had been taking your car into the same garage for years, liking the people there and relying on them to look after you. Then, one day, you overhear the boss whispering to a mechanic to fit a suspect, second rate spare part in your car… because you're the kind of dope that would never know the difference. How would you feel now? That it's an insignificant theft of a few pounds? Perhaps a little let down? Or that it's a shocking betrayal of your trust, and that you'd never feel safe using that garage again?

Or, more sadly, how do married couples react when their partners stray? Is the behaviour met with a shrug at a minor departure from the benefits of pair bonding

- or is it seen as a complete betrayal of the marital faithfulness people thought came with the most important cooperative relationship of their lives?

Insights like these now began to influence researchers into changing the rules for their iterated prisoner's dilemma trials. New rounds of tests included the objective of seeing if strangers would behave differently if they'd had the opportunity *to assess each other* before the games started. Would people's decisions change if they were given the chance to form an opinion of their 'opponent' before they settled down to play?

The results were astonishing. In short, they revealed just how brilliant our natural human ability is to predict another person's character. If test subjects met for only a few minutes, or even *seconds* before the tests began, they showed an almost uncanny knack of forecasting how their opponents would play.

Should we be too surprised at this though? Most of us already think our intuition means we can sum up other people in a glance. Malcolm Gladwell describes the process in his extraordinary book on gut reactions, *Blink*, as the result of intelligence, experience, and of particular rules and principles that lead to a '... magical and mysterious thing called judgement'.

'We need to respect the fact that it is possible to know without knowing why we know and to accept that - sometimes - we're better off that way... We really only trust conscious decision-making. But there are moments... (when) decisions made very quickly can be every bit as good as decisions made cautiously and deliberately.'
Malcolm Gladwell, *Blink*

Although much of this process plainly comes from our unconscious, researchers found that if contestants instinctively felt they could trust each other, then they almost immediately set aside trying to grind one another down, or even protecting themselves from losing points. Instead, they'd embark on treating each other as rational actors who were capable of forming collaborative relationships. Guessing at the other contestant's reputation, picking up clues about what kind of person he was, and acting on seen or unseen insights, were all critical to arriving at the level of trust needed for reaching out to the other side.

These sorts of tactics were now being defined by game theorists as the '*shadow of the future*'. By this they meant the way our imaginations could drive an intuitive and continuous weighing up of risk and reward, judgement and vision that was part stealth, part defensiveness, part gambit and wholly strategic. How very, very clever we are, it was increasingly becoming apparent - far cleverer than we could ever have imagined.

Just as we could work out for ourselves what our own strategies should be, we were also able to understand the logic that was driving other people's as well. And the key to this reasoning was our ability to project forward in our minds to see what the *consequences* were of us making different choices.

Alongside this, however, game theorists were also now seeing that there could similarly be benefits from *not playing the game*. That was because, in a world of rational tactics and mutual understanding, there would always be personalities who had the capacity to blow up the whole process by stubbornly refusing to follow the logic of expected interactions.

What are they doing though? Well, sometimes, it seems hard to know. There are occassions when they appear to be unhinged or just wildly erratic, sometimes they're even in danger of pulling the whole system of reasoned exchange down around their ears. But here's the strange thing… they often get results.

What was plain, social scientists were now saying, was that lunatic actions could have such a shocking effect that they'd unsettle the other side… and that this kind of irrationality could prove to be a profitable gambit. Volatile and illogical people who played in this way were now being described as 'madmen'. Nonetheless, they were frequently showing their ability to use seemingly irrational behaviour to get rewards in what were otherwise predictable negotiations.

Donald Trump. A madman?

People like this put others on the back foot. That's because we generally like to live with certainties and reason, and most of us dislike disorder and confusion. But these 'madmen' actively sow discord because they upset the odds. Machiavelli famously said that '… it is a wise thing to stimulate madness' because one's enemies were never sure of how far they could go before some kind of explosion could carry *everyone* away.

Richard Nixon, for example, had been weirdly unpredictable during his negotiations with the North Vietnamese, yet he managed to achieve a better than expected outcome as he tried to bring the war to a close. Similarly, Donald Trump would frequently employ the 'madman' tactic to destabilise the opposition, and it would work because most people are understandably fearful of irrational intransigence.

When you're dealing with someone that you think cares more about ruining you than any concern he might have for his own potential self-destruction, then we tread very carefully indeed. Perhaps the prime example of our age is Vladimir Putin, a man who seems to threaten to resolve every conflict by resorting to nuclear warfare, even though this would guarantee the end of the Russian people as well. Yet he manages to worry us more even than his Communists forebears did, because he's constantly shown himself to be so utterly disdainful of human life, and yet be so thin skinned and volatile, that the world treats him with the softest of kid gloves.

Not for nothing did game theorists now begin to label the madman's approach and other kinds of seemingly irrational choices as a 'trembling hand', because these dangerous types could potentially pull the carpet out from under other people just as easily as they could follow a more understandable strategy.

> **'Game theory… only works when people play games rationally. So it can't predict the behaviour of love-sick teenagers like Romeo and Juliet or madmen like Hitler or Stalin.'**
> **Ken Binmore, *Game Theory***

Setting these impossible characters to one side, however, it was now plain that if one wanted to succeed by forming relationships - and therefore to build the order and reliability of a society - then cooperation had to be the right strategy. It was by using a vision of the future that people would be incentivised to play high scoring games with each other - games in which they were collaborating at best, or simply living to fight another day at worst - rather than worrying about being beaten.

When they did this, they were setting out to win wars, not battles, because cooperators knew that they were going to carry on meeting the same people, and would be continuing to deal with them over long periods of time.

Rather than being seduced by the opportunity to win points by snatching at sneaky defections, they didn't need to be told that one good turn deserves another. Instead, they'd realise that burning out their relationships with a quick stab in the back might give them an easy few points, but it would also lead to trust being lost, and punishments coming down on them until it could be restored.

Perhaps most surprisingly for the researchers, contestants seemed to instinctively recognise that it was the *collective score* that mattered more than the individual totals... just as staying silent would have profited both prisoners if they could only have trusted each other.

Here were exposed the building blocks that resolve the eternal conundrum between the rights of the individual and the rights of society. People would use their choices to say where they wanted society to go... and every indication was that their overall wish was for a fair, open, non-zero, trust-based, bottom-up system.

The structure of the prisoner's dilemma had been remarkably fruitful in spelling out the nuances of cooperative, two person games. The mathematical findings were plainly illustrating the critical importance of forming repetitive, stable relationships that would result in shared benefits within safe, stable communities. Reputations, trust and the frequency of exchange all evidently come together in a strongly bonded society, and once secured, interpersonal exchanges could quickly evolve into the ideal state of *Always Cooperate*.

When this happened, like-minded people could exchange their three points with each other over long periods of time. Six point relationships would bloom, and society would benefit because social efficiency was the end result.

All good, you might think. And surely Always Cooperate is another way of describing the benefits that Adam Smith saw as coming from free markets... that if you let people deal freely and openly in society, then they'll settle down into looking after each other, because it was in their self-interests to do so? Game theory was coming up with precisely the same 'bottom-up' finding.

Aaarh. Long sigh of satisfaction. How nice to come to this conclusion.

So what could possibly go wrong?

**You might not think it, but this Hawk could be
making a bad mistake.**

The Secrets of Life - Book Three

GAME THEORISTS WERE SEEING THE RESULTS OF THE ITERATED PRISONER'S DILEMMA AS CONFIRMING THE INEVITABLE SUCCESS OF COOPERATION. BUT CAN THAT REALLY BE RIGHT? SURELY THERE'S EVIDENCE OF THE OPPOSITE WHEREVER WE LOOK? BULLIES, STRONG MEN AND HORRIBLE TYPES SO OFTEN SEEM TO WIN IN LIFE RATHER THAN THE NICE GUYS. SO WHAT'S GOING ON?

Adam Smith had famously ended up by saying that if humans were only allowed to get on and deal with each other - as long as good laws and credible information protected them - then a natural process of specialisation and exchange would create cooperative and fair societies.

But what he'd also seen was that the more trusting and moral a community might be, the easier it was for cheats and non-contributors to take advantage of it. Sadly, game theory was now exposing precisely the same flaw. Simulated outcomes of the Dilemma were showing that defectors could easily take advantage of an open and collaborative society - whether it was by selling bad beef, running an investment scam or flirting with someone else's wife.

The temptation to grab easy points is inevitable. And it's as present in human exchanges as it is in the natural world - where sharp practice and double-crossing are to be seen everywhere one looks. In fact, cheating is as much a feature of bacterial, plant and animal life as it is in our own relationships.

Game theorists now began to refer to the milder of the five point grabbers who undermined society as 'free riders'. These are people who take advantage of the trust levels so necessary in a cooperative community, but who don't pay their fair share. Like what?

Well, take a person who jumps the barrier at a railway station and hops on a train without a ticket. Now this would seem to be a pretty minor offence, hardly worth bothering with. The train was going anyway and if the man had forked up for a fare he'd have only made a tiny contribution to the running costs. What possible harm could come from not paying?

But there is harm. Society is diminished because he's done something that if *everyone did it* then the consequences would be disastrous.

In fact, any situation in which one might be tempted to do something - yet if it became a generally accepted practice the outcome would be highly destructive - is likely to be a form of prisoner's dilemma.

And the free rider has also done huge harm to himself. The other passengers would see that he'd cheated, and they'd now know him for the thief that he is. He's given up his right to be trusted for the sake of a few coins.

This kind of behaviour doesn't particularly matter to him when he's never going to see the people again, but if he'd done the same thing in a small community - perhaps at work or in a hunter-gatherer society - then his reputation would be damaged disproportionately to the crime. The news would be spread around by our human appetite for gossip and, very possibly, exaggerated in the retelling.

Social scientists see this as a modern version of Rousseau's stag hunt: a minor event that suggests a major flaw. Trust is hard to build and yet easily damaged. We view the behaviour of others in small matters almost as more indicative of character than in large ones. 'If he can pull the wings off a butterfly, think what he'd do to someone he didn't like.'

Yet minor misdeeds are more easily excused in larger societies than small ones. There was some recent polling in the *London Evening Standard*, for example, that showed a quarter of all respondents thought, even today, that fare dodging was a 'victimless crime'. Presumably, they didn't think through to the implication of a quarter of the population actually doing it.

Game theorists were concluding that their investigations into the impact of free riders and other defector opportunities, anxieties about fair division such as the Ultimatum and Dictator games, and particularly the more subtle workings of the prisoner's dilemma, all seemed to be revealing a great insight.

Surely, ran their conclusions, they were all versions of what happened when collective and individual interests were in conflict? What they all seemed to be illustrating was that the winning strategies were those based on projecting forward to the future - and seeing how one's actions would influence it. This is a function of our intuitive human ability to imagine what's going to happen when we're dealing with people.

In short, it's our capacity to use logic to weigh things up that separates us from all the other organisms in life.

This endless envisaging of the future is instinctive and unconscious; operating in less time than it takes to click one's fingers. Yet it means that we're able to guess at what the consequences are likely to be of our words and actions - and how others will react to them. From this we can shape our behaviour accordingly.

If you take the mechanism of the Dilemma as an example, we're able to see that rewards come to those who can trust someone enough to collaborate with them. The right thing to do depends on what the other person does - and if they want to cooperate then we'll usually go along with it.

But are we doing this because we're nice and falling in with the wishes of the other man? Or are we doing it because we're looking out for ourselves… collecting points in other words?

How might all this be summed up? Well, is it possible to come to any other conclusion than that whatever our true thoughts, *we wish to appear to be cooperative, to be unselfish, but only because we selfishly want the benefits that doing so will bring.*

We behave like this because we intuitively know that collaborating is a winning strategy in life. We're therefore trying to look after ourselves… yet we've worked out that the best way to do this is to be selfless, even though we know that we're doing this out of self-interest. This is similar to the logic that Bill Hamilton used when he came to the awful conclusion that 'altruism is just genetic selfishness'.

The inescapable conclusion that game theory was now presenting was that the reason we're virtuous in life is because we are calculating, selfish organisms, whose base motive is to survive and prosper. What an awful paradox. The implication of this undeniable reasoning has to be that it's our profound need for social collaboration that's driving our inexplicably empathetic natures.

> **'What makes the existence and the evolution of society possible is precisely**
> **the fact that peaceful cooperation under the social division of labour in the**
> **long run best serves the selfish concerns of individuals.'**
> **Ludwig von Mises,** *Liberalism*

Surely here is 'Das Adam Smith Problem' run to ground?

Smith had struggled to explain that his description of our instinct for self-interest didn't conflict with his principle that humans obviously care about the fortunes and happiness of others. Not to do so was almost the definition of a sociopath. Yet he and his later followers were to spend decades trying to explain the dissonance away.

Now game theory was leading researchers to the solution. They were showing that the way we humans had absorbed the survival mechanisms of our ancestors meant that we'd discovered, over the evolution of our species, that care for others is a natural consequence of our rational desire for mutually beneficial, sharing societies - and for all the efficiencies and security that go with them.

To put this at its starkest... we may have begun as selfish organisms, just vehicles for our selfish genes, but we've now evolved to the point where we can describe cooperation as an essentially moral force. In fact this has become such a deeply held meme that it's now 'the right way to behave'.

> **'Nothing truly valuable can be achieved except by the**
> **unselfish cooperation of many individuals.'**
> **Albert Einstein**

It's a kind of filmic cliché that if you went back to the Stone Age in a time machine, you'd see the woolly-headed barbarians reacting with pleasure to modern man's proffered exchanges and kindness, particularly if things were held out to them by a beautiful actress. But I rather doubt the idea.

Instead, any time travellers that were strolling around would probably have had their heads bashed in by people who'd never have understood that strangers could be anything but dangerous. It's second nature to us now to deal with others, and we've become very, very good at it... but it's a learned behaviour, a concept that's evolved with our development. And it's one that's largely driven by the success of our cultural development.

All very interesting, you may be thinking, but doesn't the whole thrust of these arguments go against the evidence of our history?

Give me a break, you'd be excused for saying, everyone knows the unpleasant truth in life - that it's the strong and nasty who win. People who care more about themselves than others. However much symbiotic gains may have evolved throughout the genetic and biological evolution of the natural world... surely the underlying story of our culture shows us becoming more selfish rather than less?

In fact, isn't the depressing reality that, in humans, the success of the power hungry, the Big Men, the snatchers, the rats who are winning the rat race... mean that the idea of cooperation just has to be wrong? Sadly, isn't the evidence of our own eyes that we humans usually behave in a pretty horrible way?

These were exactly the kind of arguments that began to push back against the theory of symbiotic gains when scientists first became interested in the reasons for our self-sacrificial behaviour. As the 1950s and 1960s unfolded, everyone from social scientists to psychologists, philosophers to popular writers like Ayn Rand, were all refusing to believe the game theorists' growing certainties. The more their research results were published, the more the hard-headed brigade maintained the line that it's tough, unsentimental, powerful people who win in life.

Forceful men succeed, they were saying, not the softer types with their misplaced attempts to share things. Nice guys, went the well-worn phrase, come second. In fact, said some, it was exactly these kinds of fluffy saps who held back human progress.

The Dilemma's counter-argument to these bitter comments was that while this might be true in *one-time* games like sporting contests and events like the Golden Balls shoot-out, it's actually the reverse that's the case in the long run of life. If one takes a distant horizon, the game theorists were now saying, it becomes increasingly clear that it's rational to be irrational - and to cooperate.

So why did the defectors win so much, would be the question in response to this? Why didn't they keep scooping 5 point gains by steam-rollering over the naive? A good point - and a real headache for game theorists - until they began to see that 'defectors' didn't all come as one type. There were shades of defection: a multitude of reasons for why people might not be as quick to collaborate as others.

At one end of a spectrum that described them, there might be individuals who were open to the idea of cooperation, but who just shied away from it because they didn't know the other side well enough to trust them. It's therefore not surprising that they'd be worried in case they were exploited.

In other words, they weren't defecting as a life policy, so much as trying to protect themselves from attack.

Then, further up the scale, there would be some who'd simply made a mistake by choosing to defect - and had then got stuck with it. Perhaps they'd arrived at their decision because they thought the other person was being too aggressive? Maybe one's opponent didn't 'feel' like a cooperative type, and until you got to know him better you'd be sensible to keep picking the default position of defecting?

At the other end of the scale are the hard nuts, the committed takers in life, people who view everyone else as fair game, and who think trusting others is for losers.

Who can blame them? The lessons of human history have always supported the approach of these sorts, and particularly Big Men and their followers. These are the people who've endlessly 'won' in life. And any bonds they ever display have always been based on fear or, at best, on a strict reciprocity with others like themselves. 'I'll do something for you as long as you do something for me' is the nearest these sorts come to cooperation, and even then any offer has to be rewarded with an immediate pay-back.

'There's plenty of evidence that we live in a reciprocating world. But, of course, it does not always follow that another player in the game of life will reciprocate. Because there is a cost involved in helping another, cooperation always comes with the threat of exploitation.'
Martin Nowak, *SuperCooperators*

These are people who are very rarely satisfied. They live in a world of believing they have the right to take things for themselves, or of 'getting even' with others. Their instinct is to put people in their place, even to crush them, if this sends out a message about how powerful they are compared to the 'losers' that surround them.

The nearest these characters ever come to collaboration is with their close family. Behaving like this has almost come to define the way monarchs, dictators and crime bosses act - a human version of the kin selection mechanism of the natural world. If you find it difficult to trust others, then the nearest you're going to get to it will be people with shared genes.

Even when they do favour their own people, though, they usually make anyone who gets something from them subservient. Looked at in this light, it's no wonder that Big Men were so vile to their subjects, why they favoured their clan, why they were anxious to stop their people from trading with strangers, and why they stamped down hard on those who ever wanted to become educated or informed.

The thing to appreciate, the game theorists were now saying, was that the selfishness and defection-saturated vision of these sorts of people understands no other way. Cooperation makes no sense to them and has no place in their lives.

The Secrets of Life - Book Three

In fact, their narcissistic belief in their right to take anything they want has become so firmly fixed in their neural programming that studies show that while people with a cooperative outlook could understand why others would want to collaborate, committed defectors, Big Men types, only understood others like themselves.

> **'Cooperative types seem to recognise the diversity of their potential competitors' approaches to the game; competitive types, however, seem to believe that all their opponents are competitive as well'**
> Edward Rosenthal *The Complete Idiot's Guide to Game Theory*

In an extreme version of this, the Irish writer, Colm Toibin highlighted the role that genetic and memetic inheritance plays in imprinting these beliefs in certain people's heads. His interest led him to research the personalities who'd been responsible for the appalling outrages of the Troubles in Northern Ireland.

What he found from talking to their neighbours and others in the community who'd known them as children, was that the bombers and murderers were every bit as angry and violent when they were young as they'd ever been when they'd joined the paramilitary forces. In other words, they were committed defectors from the start, blindly selfish sorts who had simply been looking for outlets to their anger. No doubt the heirs to great positions in society were brought up to have a similar sense of entitlement.

But the question remained - why didn't these people always win?

They had the power, they had the ruthless streak, they had the motives, and they were convinced they had the *right* to be superior.

To answer this, game theorists now began to label these sorts of people as Hawks… amoral and focussed attack machines. On the other hand, people who were naturally cooperative when they played the prisoner's dilemma were described as Doves. This distinction, researchers felt, faithfully reflected the polarity of people's views in real life.

So, what happened over the long run as computer modelling looked at how this mix of strategies evolved? What emerged if the IPD was played without an end point?

First, of course, the Hawks won. They easily scored more highly than cooperators, constantly playing 'Defect' and refusing to respond to any attempt at collaboration. On and on they'd go, snaffling up five points whenever someone was foolish enough to hold out a collaborative hand, but never dropping beneath the one point they'd chalk up if they were met by defection in return.

Before long, the Hawks were so successful that they'd hugely reduce the proportion of sharing types in the population. But then the cost of doing this began to show up. Because they'd killed so many Doves, or forced them to flee, those that remained were reduced to very small numbers... and the consequence of this was that *Hawks now inevitably kept meeting people like themselves.*

What then? Well, the Hawks now fought the other Hawks. They knew no other way, of course, they only understood conflict. They had no instinct for cooperation. Naturally, before long, they'd reduced their numbers by eliminating each other. And it was at this point that a certain kind of Dove now started to fight back.

Game theorists called these characters 'Retaliator Doves', and the Dilemma showed them as achieving two unexpected results.

First, they'd fight like a Hawk and could neutralise the real Hawks if they had to.

But secondly, they'd cooperate if they met other Doves. In this way they would begin to gradually haul in the Hawks because they were getting six points from their Dovish encounters, instead of the five points or one point outcomes that were all the Hawks could ever expect from defection.

This might seem a little complicated, but the computer simulations were showing exactly the picture one sees repeatedly throughout our history. When certain kinds of peace-loving people are faced with the threat of annihilation, they can become surprisingly warlike and Hawkish.

'A retaliator behaves like a hawk when he is attacked by a hawk, and like a dove when he meets a dove. When he meets another retaliator he plays like a dove. A retaliator is a conditional strategist. His behaviour depends on the behaviour of his opponent.'
Richard Dawkins, *The Selfish Gene*

The human evolutionary story has always shown that over the long run of our existence, Retaliator Doves like this will inevitably beat the Hawks. How's that possible?

Well, first, because an existential crisis often leads to them 'burning the boats', and putting aside their lives of repeated collaboration, they now focus on a single-minded drive to drive back the enemy. Instead of playing Cooperate in an iterated prisoner's dilemma, they deliberately turn their lives into a series of one-time encounters.

Secondly, they win because they're now working together with others like themselves. Once they find other collaborators, they'll operate in teams in which everyone shares a focussed commitment to beating the Hawks. United in this way, they'll exhibit such fierce loyalty to each other that they're prepared to sacrifice themselves for the common good, showing their best qualities and a shared moral vision.

This altruistic impulse is working in exactly the way it does when social insects and bacteria give away their lives so their genes can be passed down by others within the species. But here, in humans, Retaliators are looking to the future and passing on their cooperative memes.

But thirdly, cooperators know how to endure. They'll keep going until they win. They're held together by strong bonds of trust, and this glues them fast to others like themselves. When they're attacked and their existence is threatened, these bonds become stronger not weaker, assuming deeper qualities like love, patriotism and a lasting belief in the family.

When Doves are placed in this position they have the common objective of outlasting the fragility of the Hawks' alliances, because these are fatally undermined by strict reciprocity, suspicion and egotism. This is what makes Hawks so rigid in the ways they behave. They have to be right all the time, and they aren't able to work collaboratively with other people in developing flexible strategies.

The things that link Hawks together are essentially selfish aims like greed, fear, blind obedience to authority and a warped belief that being powerful means automatically winning by crushing collaborative types. But they're wrong. Connections like these are all built on selfishness, while Doves will bring a vision of a better future and a group ability to adjust their tactics as they push for victory.

How often has the world seen the result? Cooperator numbers may initially be small, but because their motivation is high, their shared linkage is indestructible. Yes, Retaliators might die for the cause, but their scale grows as defector societies are eaten away by their own shortcomings.

Mathematical modelling of the iterated prisoner's dilemma illustrates that over the long-term, the sheer collaborative power of Retaliator Doves leads them to victory. In case after case, researchers were watching their computer screens in fascination as cooperator numbers grew in simulated gameplay, and the mathematical logic of continuous six point combinations inevitably overcame the limited defector totals of the Hawks' behaviour.

Historians and social theorists were now viewing how this emerging picture reflected the arc of human development. They could now see that the greater the chance of collaborative people finding each other, the more that Big Men had been, and would be, undermined.

Taken over the length of our existence, our history shows that their bullying superiority had been largely unchallenged until agriculture weakened their hold with the growth of larger societies. They'd held on at this point by dominating others with laws, religion and the sword. But Retaliator Doves then increasingly changed society by using the collective benefits that came from trading, and the collaborative power of specialisation and exchange.

Gradually, cooperation had grown as trustworthy information and efficient transport became more widespread. Our cultural direction, social scientists were now saying, showed that Hawks might be uncontested at overcoming the 1st Law, but it was Doves who would meet the challenges of the 2nd. Thermodynamics, in other words, had been governing our human development every bit as much as it had shaped evolution in the natural world.

And all the time this was going on, the underlying path of our cultural dynamic has been constantly reducing the Big Man's Hawk-like presumption of authority. Because of this, it's hardly surprising that as hawkish instincts were being reduced, philosophers and religious thinkers were formalising the outcomes into a set of moral standards. The memes that arose over time reinforced cooperation as the right way to ensure societies became productive and avoided the entropic results of selfish instincts.

This is the reasoning that lies behind our ethical standards: our natural laws, the codes governing our social interactions, and our collective sense of civilised behaviour. All stem from the same game theoretic logic.

So, what's the end of the story?

The Hawks and Doves illustration shows how the powerless become powerful by working together and why, ultimately… cooperation wins. The Hawks might initially have looked like winners, but in time they're undermined by their own behaviour. Conversely, losers could come together to become winners. The result, as Margaret

Thatcher was once reputed to have uttered: '… as Jesus said - and I must say I thought he was *particularly sound* on this point - 'the meek shall inherit the earth."

What happened to the Retaliator Doves? Well, once the long battle was over and the high scoring games returned, they quickly reverted to Dovish behaviour. They returned to making gains with each other through the synergistic benefits of Always Cooperate. We always think of 'meek' as meaning lowly or downtrodden, but when one equates it with openness and cooperation, it all makes sense. With Sauron dead, Mordor defeated and the Ring destroyed, the Retaliator Dove Hobbits went back to their contented, cooperative lives in the Shire.

But hold on a minute, surely there are other Hawks coming along to take the place of the losers? After all, it's not as if there aren't still masses of them around.

That's true, but the story of our human existence is that their presence has been diminishing. This is because cooperative people will avoid them once it becomes obvious that any attempt at collaborating with them will always be rebuffed. Think about one's own life - how many times would you try to share with people that are consistently hostile to you in return?

Our history has seen Hawk-like Big Men succeed because the people they had control over simply couldn't escape their suffocating rules and paranoia inspired bullying. The Dilemma might suggest we should avoid them, but for most of our history this was simply impossible to do because these types wouldn't let you go. They demanded obedience, but they only achieved this by instilling fear-laden cultures and the threat of violent retribution.

And even if cooperators managed to somehow get away from these horrible people, they'd probably have then become subjected to the same kind of top-down treatment from another Big Man. It was almost impossible in the past to exist outside the orbit of someone throwing his weight around, and imposing his zero sum outlook on the world.

But, as the great Harvard psychologist, Stephen Pinker says in his extraordinary book on violence, *The Better Angels of Our Nature*: 'Everything in human affairs is connected to everything else, and that is especially true of violence. Across time and space, the more peaceable societies also tend to be richer, healthier, better educated, better governed, more respectful of their women, and more likely to engage in trade. Positive-sum games also change the incentives for violence. If you're trading favours or surpluses with someone, your trading partner suddenly becomes more valuable to you alive than dead.'

The growth of trading, information, transport, prosperity and education have all had profound effects on our human development. We take these things for granted now, but it's only very recently in our cultural evolution that we've started to make free choices about our futures.

Instead of a defector mindset being the necessary first stage to becoming a Big Man, this is often now a painful burden because it can lead to a bad reputation, to unpopularity and to social exclusion. It also logically results in fewer of one's genes being passed on. Finding a mate becomes harder, defectors' offspring are likely to be excluded as well, the long squeeze on their numbers is underway… in short, it's evolutionary suicide when looked at over long enough periods of time.

The converse of all this is that cooperation is an evolutionary inevitability. How Prince Kropotkin would have smiled if he'd seen the result of the computer simulations of the iterated prisoner's dilemma. He'd come to his conclusions in *Mutual Aid* largely on the basis of observation, a full sixty years before anyone could ever have dreamt of the mathematical logic of game theory. And yet, this new way of seeing strategic decision-making was to prove the accuracy of his most famous conclusion that: *'the*

Game theory in action.

The Secrets of Life - Book Three

most successful species are the most cooperative'.

Is this such a weird conclusion to come to? Is it really so hard for us to accept? I know, it sure seems a foolhardy assumption as one wearily witnesses the bastards who are so often running things in our lives. Don't unspeakable people still seem to get to the top of the ladders in life rather too often? And aren't they frequently running organisations in the most greedy way, shifting questionable stuff onto unsuspecting people, and persisting in finding like-minded cronies to line each other's pockets?

But the point is… not everyone is like this. We now know what the bad ones look like. We've developed mechanisms for identifying them, ways of warning each other, and judicial systems designed to punish them.

When we're left to our own devices we've developed laws that protect the unwary, we pass on information about the behaviour of wrong 'uns, we write reviews, we create regulatory systems, and we do the million and one other things that shape a world of avoidance and the punishment of abuse.

The entire direction of our cultural development has been to arrive at philosophies that promote benevolent and admirable behaviour - and condemn selfishness and ego-driven control. Above all, we've formalised what humans have come to regard as the *right* decisions to make - and lumped them together and called it morality.

This moral thinking has become so deeply ingrained in our neural programming that we endlessly perform unnecessary acts that reinforce our own internalised sense of fairness and concern for others.

We tip waiters we'll never see again, we donate to causes that will never thank us, we carry out unseen acts of compassion and, yes, we value altruism as the most noble of human qualities. All these sorts of things are filling up some kind of imaginary weighing pan in our brains, tipping the balance of self-assessment towards the 'good' side in the scale of life. The reasons we do this, we now know, originate from the instructions of our selfish genes, but hey, what does that matter?

> **'The emotions are problem-solving devices designed to make (us)**
> **highly social creatures effective at using social relations to their genes'**
> **long-term advantage. They are a way of settling the conflict between**
> **short-term expediency and long-term prudence in favour of the latter.'**
> **Matt Ridley, *The Origins of Virtue***

And yet we have to admit that the struggle continues. A little angel with wings is on one shoulder, and another with a pitchfork is on the other. Both of them are endlessly whispering in our ears. The temptation to grab five points is ever present, yet we still often manage to resist the temptations of the bad guy.

Yes, there may be obvious rewards to be had from defecting - but cooperators are the people who get to sleep at night. They're content they've done the right thing. If they're dealing with people they like and trust, they win. If not, then they're still likely to be soundly snoring, knowing that the 'Impartial Spectator' is tipping his hat at them.

More importantly than that, quite a few of us think this is how we'll get to heaven. Just as we bargain with each other, don't so many of us also bargain with God?

What are all those entreaties, prayers, promises and sacrifices if they're not a kind of spiritual deal-making in which 'the shadow of the future' is shaping the landscape of our morality? And just how true is the reverse? How often do the 'unlovely and unloved' think that religion is simply an absurd construct for the weak minded?

But if the underlying vector of where the prisoner's dilemma takes us has been to show that the evolution of human cooperation is a directional force... is it one we've inherited from our animal ancestors? Does the same direction of history show up in the glacial mutational changes that have kept life on earth going, often in the teeth of catastrophic environmental changes that periodically threaten to wipe everything out?

The entire story of evolution would seem to illustrate it is. Major transitions all relied on the cooperation of different elements. Indeed, we're built by cooperation - actually made of cells that are working together for their mutual benefit. We're no different to anything else on the Behavioural Spectrum that shows how organisms engage in symbiotic endeavours.

Many of the early chapters of these books were spent in showing how the root cause of all decision-making, both in Nature and in us humans, lies with that staggeringly brilliant and inventive string-puller, the gene.

The gene may have been described as 'selfish' in that it's finding vehicles to ensure it survives, but to do this it has also created mechanisms that arrived at the fittest life forms. In doing this it's choosing the optimal ways of getting the most genes out into the gene pool. And cooperation is what lies behind this logic.

Yet this still leaves a big question. If the prisoner's dilemma shows how non-zero sum strategies can win in life... how do living things decide on whether they can work together?

How can they get the benefits that are on offer from collaboration - yet avoid the dangers of being exploited or cheated?

An early researcher is about to push a button
to see if the secrets of life come out.

CHAPTER NINE

SURVIVING, COMPETING, COOPERATING, TRUSTING, CHEATING, PROTECTING ONESELF, SUCCEEDING IN THE FITNESS WAR. . . ALL THE ANCIENT DRIVES USED BY LIVING THINGS WERE NOW BEING EXPOSED TO GAME THEORY'S GAZE. BUT COULD THE PRISONER'S DILEMMA SHOW HOW THEY ALL FITTED TOGETHER?

As the Swinging Sixties began to shade into the rather odder Seventies, large numbers of academics were hammering away at their computers, sharing in the fun of exploring just how far the prisoner's dilemma could take them in answering the most profound questions of their different disciplines.

Everyone had come to agree that the gains available from cooperation were what had built life on earth. And everyone could see that the Dilemma's big message was that Always Cooperate allowed trust to grow, and led to individual organisms achieving repeated gains.

But that still left the problem of how to stop others from cheating. And not only that, but why wouldn't everything cheat when the temptation to snaffle a five point advantage in a trusting world was always so seductive? Punishments for defecting, of course, slowed this down, but wasn't it better to stop this kind of thing happening in the first place?

Put bluntly, could fear ever completely overcome greed?

> 'It's just as foolish to complain that people are selfish or treacherous as it is
> to complain that the magnetic field has a curl. Both are laws of nature.'
> **John von Neumann,** *Year Book of the American Philosophical Society*

The conclusions coming through from researchers who were using humans as research guinea pigs were interesting. But questions were increasingly being asked about whether these same results could also explain some of the more intractable mysteries of our biological heritage.

If we'd evolved from a long line of earlier life forms, did this mean that the way humans behaved shone a light on the actions of organisms in the natural world? Could this be the case when our species alone had the ability to chop and change our behaviour based on flashes of intuition and our vision of the future? But how could other things be expected to behave rationally when they didn't come equipped with our kind of brain?

Three centuries earlier, Galileo had talked about how 'the laws of nature are written by the hand of God in the language of mathematics' and now biologists and evolutionary theorists were taking the old boy at his word. Pounding away at the Dilemma with increasingly adventurous computer programmes, biologists were now endlessly exploring the ways that different motivations operated.

How, they wanted to know, was it possible for organisms to get the most points from dividing their labour and specialising their skills - and yet to remain on the lookout for the exploitation that could come from the inevitable cheats? Researchers were seeing how humans weighed up the odds and judged each other - but was it possible that lower organisms could be doing the same thing?

Life forms that offered aid to one another are to be seen everywhere in the natural world. But doing this always seemed to deny the rationale of Darwinian natural selection. Behaving in a way that sacrificed a part of one's fitness to help something else that was acting selfishly would seem to be the quickest way to a selective *disadvantage*. Yet it was to be seen everywhere there were groups and colonies.

A pack of dingoes for example, would have its individual members cooperating when they were out hunting for much needed meat. If one looked closely, though, there'd always be some that were doing more than their share of the hard work, and some that would be behaving like the dog equivalents of free riders.

By hanging back and avoiding the dangers of bringing down the prey, the duckers in the pack would be sharing in the spoils and yet cutting down on their injury risks. As the brave, reckless contributors were more likely to be killed or maimed by going in where it hurt, it logically followed that the cheats would be at a relative fitness advantage... and, therefore, that defector genes should flourish at the expense of the altruistic.

But field research was now showing that these cheats were actually being *spotted and identified* by other members of the group. Just as in human societies, they were being seen for who they were, and then being excluded, shunned, stopped from feeding early and generally being branded as unwelcome.

The consequence was the same as with us humans - being a regarded as a loser meant that finding a mate became more difficult. Instead of the defector genes being replicated, it was actually more likely that they'd be winnowed out of the gene pool. Set against this, the same evolutionary logic meant that the altruistic genes in the pack were bound to increase… and that cooperation would *expand*.

Before these conclusions were being proposed, Bill Hamilton had famously shown how the same process works to make altruistic genes dominate in intensely collaborative groups like eusocial insect colonies. Hamilton's Rule was now accepted as illustrating that although an individual might elect to reduce its own fitness, and to boost that of a sibling's, by being altruistic it was actually *increasing* the number of genes that flowed through to the next generation.

This was the gene at its most subtle… using cooperation to ensure that copies of the genes that helped its survival would flourish.

What biologists were now seeing was just how much this process was being predicted by the Dilemma. Altruism was cooperation, cheating was defection. Altruism led to players sharing six points, cheating never got more than five. If the game was iterated, played repeatedly, then altruism would evolve… as long as there was a statistical likelihood that the beneficiaries would be altruists themselves.

Now researchers began to ask themselves if it was possible that the same mechanism might be taking place between living things that *weren't related, and therefore weren't genetically linked.*

But surely this made no sense at all? Why would an organism suffer a fitness loss to help something else when it had no investment in its genes? What could possibly be in it for them?

Yet everywhere one looked in the natural world there were examples of both related and non-related altruism. There were, of course, symbiotic unions to be seen - but the participants in these had, for better or worse, become stuck in their tight little arrangements. In fact, their lives had become so entwined that they could no longer live without each other.

But why did things that were biologically and genetically different help each other?

To answer this, researchers now began to turn their focus towards organisms that were behaving like us humans in making partnership decisions. Why did so many animals, for example, waste good hunting time on grooming each other? Why did organisms share their food, or remove each other's parasites and so on? Sometimes these were *within* the same species - like a group of related chimpanzees picking bugs out of one another - but sometimes they were between wholly *separate species*. What was going on?

> 'Biologists have a huge advantage over social scientists in applying game theory, because they have so much more data. Natural selection has generated a vast variety of different species, some of which are so weird and wonderful that they seem to defy rational explanation.'
> Ken Binmore, *Game Theory*

This was a particularly appropriate question to be asking at this time, because by the end of the 1960s the leading expert on animal behaviour was reckoned to be a man called Konrad Lorenz. In 1966 he'd published a major work on aggression and many people had been influenced by reading his view that animals were biologically programmed to fight, most notably when they came under population stress, or were squabbling to share a fixed resource.

Although Lorenz would later win the Nobel Prize for Medicine in 1973, it would be charitable to say he was an acquired taste. An ex-member of the Nazi party and an apologist for eugenics, he seemed to represent the confusion of opinions that were struggling to understand the appalling slaughter of the Second World War. Game theorists were now adding their own opinions that this might have been the ultimate example of Retaliator Doves collaborating to defeat the Hawkish philosophies of Germany and Japan.

Nonetheless, Lorenz was arguing that a species progressed by the process of having the strongest and most aggressive males mating with pliable, passive females. Hmm. With the perspective of history, this seems a very fascistic viewpoint, even from someone who had denounced its role in Nazi doctrines.

In his defence, Lorenz was working from field observation, and showed no appreciation of the gene-based theory of evolution. Instead, he was convinced that what benefited a species was what drove its genes.

This made him a committed proponent of the 'group selection' school of thought, and it was hardly surprising, therefore, that later 'kin selection' biologists like Richard

Dawkins and EO Wilson, were to label him as 'essentially wrong'.

In spite of this, Lorenz had an enormous influence on the ongoing debate about whether man's biological heritage had ended up by making him into a terrible being, incapable of generosity or altruism unless the behaviour had a competitive objective. And, if *we* were so bad, went the logic, then it was no wonder that people were pulling faces at the idea that lower organisms - where we'd come from - would ever actually *help* each other.

Now another giant figure was going to join the story. And, what a strange fellow he was, and remains so to this day. If ever someone could be said to have strongly opposed Hawkish and Dovish aspects to his personality, it would be him. Turbulent and much troubled, he's now recognised as an extraordinary genius whose creative instincts and fearless attitudes have consistently overturned conventional beliefs.

He's an American called Robert Trivers - still only in his late seventies - and among the depth charges he was to chuck into the evolutionary biology world was to use the iterated prisoner's dilemma as a way of showing how different forms of cooperation

**Robert Trivers in the early 1970s. He liked to
sleep surrounded by books and papers.**

lie at the heart of success in *non-human* life forms.

Stephen Pinker's in no doubt that he's been 'one of the greatest thinkers of Western thought' yet Robert Trivers's life has been a volcanic mix of mental illness, prestigious prizes, academic and physical fights, armed hold-ups, drug addictions, prison time and a high-profile association with Huey Newton, the leader of the Black Panthers.

His restless nature has been both a curse and a blessing. He began his time at Harvard studying pure maths, then switched to physics, then to the law, then history and, finally, to genetics.

What he 'fell in love with', according to an article in the *Guardian*, 'was the flow of genes through generations and the steady, inexorable shaping of behaviour by natural selection.'

Along the way of his early career he suffered a series of debilitating breakdowns that produced the diagnosis of a severe bi-polar condition. Yet this astonishing cocktail of forces led him, as a twenty-seven year old without even a completed doctorate, to publish five papers during a manic period in 1971 that explained why our human obsession with fairness, jealousy, cooperation and justice had a Darwinian logic to it.

More than that, he was to show that many of our behavioural drives made the same genetic sense in lower organisms as they did in us. It was rather like Beethoven writing his six piano concertos in a fortnight.

Among his papers were breathtakingly original insights on sex ratios, the attractiveness of symmetrical features, the reasons for parent and offspring conflict, and then one that demolished Lorenz's arguments about male dominance.

This last went on to play a role in the feminist movement by showing how females have to invest more in the process of mate selection than males, because they can only have a child every few months while men can initiate any number of pregnancies during the same time. This, he proposed, was a genetic explanation for much of the behavioural antipathy between the two genders.

But it was arguably the first of the five papers that most greatly challenged evolutionary theory. In this, Trivers used the findings of the iterated prisoner's dilemma in humans to argue that exactly the same kinds of outcomes took place in the natural world. He described the way that individual organisms exchange benefits as: '*reciprocal altruism*', and to prove why this occurred, he took a mathematical approach to showing that while there might be a genetic cost to helping others, it still paid non-related organisms to do so… *if there was an expectation of getting something back in return.*

'Trivers was the first to establish the importance of the repeated - also known as the iterated - prisoner's dilemma for biology, so that in a series of encounters between animals, cooperation is able to emerge.'
Martin Nowak, *SuperCooperators*

Unlike Bill Hamilton's explanation for kin selective altruism, Trivers hypothesised that there was no need for two cooperative individuals wanting mutual benefits to be related within a species… *or even to be members of the same species at all.*

The critical issues, he said, were that just as in human synergies, if things dealt over long enough periods of time - and had the ability to recognise one another so they could monitor how they each behaved - then they'd be able to identify and punish cheats - and also those who failed to punish cheats.

'The most direct way to encourage cooperation is to make the interactions more durable.'
Robert Axelrod, *The Evolution of Cooperation*

This all sounds a lot like us, except we've taken the mechanism on a lot further. We humans have intelligence, the ability to recognise faces, the use of language to pass on gossip about people's reputations and, perhaps most importantly, the capacity to imagine what others are thinking.

As the social scientist, Robert Axelrod says, we are unlike other organisms in that we have: '… a more complex memory, more complex processing of information (with which) to determine the next action as a function of the interaction so far, a better estimate of the probability of future interaction with the same individual and a better ability to distinguish between different individuals.'

'In humans (reciprocal altruism) is well developed and is largely based on the recognition of faces.'
Robert Axelrod, *The Evolution of Cooperation*

This means that we're constantly projecting into the future to weigh up the benefits that can come from reciprocal actions. Defectors, for example, want benefits returned immediately. Many of the rest of us, however, are playing a longer game, deliberately not snatching at being paid back.

Instead, we're allowing little debts and favours to build up in the expectation that things will come out in the wash if we've been right about those we think we can trust.

But just how cross do we get when it turns out the weighing up process has got out of whack? Our sense of fairness and justice becomes outraged if what we're giving isn't being rewarded, or if we discover we've been taken advantage of.

Trivers' insight was to see that organisms in the natural world didn't have our capacity for delayed exchange. They couldn't 'keep the score' or make a decision about waiting a little longer to be repaid. Yes, they could be open to the gains that were possible from cooperation, but there had to be conditions.

First, Trivers said, the arrangement had to suit both parties in such a way that it was 'agreed'. If that was the case, then a helpful act had to be returned immediately. 'You do something, and I'll do something back' was the deal, and not 'it'll all come right in the end'.

The second requirement was that organisms, just like us, had to be able to spot defectors. There had to be a threat hanging over potential cheats. If things were going to fake their side of the deal or evade the bargain, then they had to run the risk of being identified. And, if they were, then they could be punished by the cascade of evolutionary exclusion and fitness loss that could follow.

Biologists began to call this process 'you scratch my back and I'll scratch yours', and many were now arguing that the logical conclusion - just as Adam Smith and the game theorists had seen in humans - *was that cooperation would inevitably evolve.*

But, you may well be asking, what kind of things did this? Organisms don't make decisions in the same way that we do, and yet Trivers was now saying that they behaved like us.

How about a few examples, people began to ask? Now field biologists knew what they were looking for, they identified them thick and fast.

One of the most elegant instances of 'within species' reciprocity was found in Costa Rica among, I'm afraid to say, vampire bats. These poor creatures (well, OK then, yuckey) only feed on the blood they've sucked out of grazing animals, and just like old Dracula, they can't last long without it. In their case, something like seventy hours at the most. And while they all fly out, looking for donors at night, some are bound to be unable to find a victim and will come back with empty tummies.

Fortunately enough, though, a bat that's had better luck can feed the ones that are going hungry. If it chooses to, it can regurgitate the blood it's taken and share it with the needy of the colony. What would the Dilemma expect now? Running the numbers would suggest that one of two things would happen. Either the 'Cooperate' request to a bat with blood to spare would get a reciprocal 'Cooperate' back from the rescued one. The expectation would then be that they, in turn, would share a good night's feed at a later date when the roles are reversed.

Or the IPD would suggest that a well-fed bat could instead decide to play 'Defect', and behave selfishly by pretending that it doesn't have any surplus. This would be an understandable strategy because the lucky bat would then be able to go longer without needing another feed. All it has to do is to give out a high-pitched squeak of 'Sorry, I don't have anything to spare.'

The twist to the story, however, is that these bats have also evolved intricate mutual grooming sessions as part of their behavioural routines. This particularly includes stroking each other around the abdomen and, if one's found to have a distended stomach, and yet has refused to share - then it's exposed as a selfish dodger. Once this happens, then the other bats shun it when it next comes back without finding a night's feed.

Evolutionary behaviour strikes again. Defectors are exposed as cheats and the genetic consequences follow. They'll be the first to die off in hungry periods, and their defector genes will inevitably leave the gene pool over evolutionary time. Cooperation, as ever, would now expand.

But what about completely *different species*? Was there similar evidence of sharing taking place among things that were wholly separate, and yet were prepared to take a loss so that something else could have a gain? Surely reciprocal altruism can't take hold when organisms have completely different lives?

And yet, it does happen - and it happens with all the sophisticated weighing up of favours that any of us humans would be proud of, whether we're splitting a bonus or deciding how we're going to divide a cream cake.

Field researchers were increasingly coming up with examples. Among the most common were the bewildering activities of one animal 'servicing' another, particularly by cleaning it or removing parasites, and biologists now began to wonder if Trivers' reciprocal altruism theory didn't provide a new insight.

What about those birds that picked food out of a crocodile's teeth as an example? They got fed and the crocs had waste removed that might have affected their health. Or the extraordinary displays seen on coral reefs where 'cleaning stations' have little fish and crustaceans that work hard giving their larger customers a wash and brush up? They get something back in return, though, because the big fish reward them by giving them a free meal and some mafia-style protection from predators.

But why don't these fish or the crocodile gobble up their little helpers once they've done their cleaning work? Some of the fishy routines can even include getting deep down into a client's mouth... what could be easier than lazily closing its jaws and swallowing them when they've finished?

It's a good question but, to ask one back, why don't you report the team of guys who rush around washing your car? Arguably it's our own version of a cleaning station. Haven't you ever sat there while they give it the once over - far more thoroughly than any machine ever could have done - and wondered just how little money they must be making? Surely, you've doubtless mused, some of them have to be illegal immigrants?

So why don't you make a fuss? Maybe even report them? You don't because they've done a great job for not a lot of money, probably better and quicker than you'd ever be able to do it. Not only are you up on the deal, but you also might think that some of them could make a real contribution to the country if they decided to stay. The outcome? You weigh things up and come to the judgement that their presence could be a benefit to society.

Big fish and other service recipients like them seem to have come to exactly the same conclusions. Customers, for example, get to know the markings of their tiny helpers and give them protection when other fish come looking for an easy meal. They let them shoot out of their mouths first, and then chase the hunters away.

On the other hand, if a cleaner fish took advantage of its client in any way, perhaps nibbling a bit of their flesh instead of a parasite, then they'll get run out of town and banned from the relationship. Once they're identified and remembered, the quid really does mean pro quo.

There are also any number of examples of reciprocal altruism in microbial societies. Some plants, for instance, allow bacteria to live in them, and in return for being given a safe home, they fix nitrogen for the host. It also goes further than that because there are even certain types of flies that then eat the bacteria as nutrients - and let them live in their digestive system.

Once the biological community knew what to look for, examples flooded in. And, of course, it wasn't long before the hair-splitters began to ask questions about what was meant by 'altruism'. Some were keen to make a distinction between the reduction of the *absolute* fitness of a donor and labelled this as 'strong' altruism, while a reduction of *relative* fitness would be enough of a difference to be labelled 'weak'.

And surely, others said as they repeated George Price's conviction about the sanctity of human thoughts and feelings... *our* kind of altruism wasn't genetically inspired at all but a higher construct altogether? Wasn't it a product of our ability to make moral judgements?

Many took completely opposing viewpoints. Their opinions were that because we rarely act without a hidden expectation of some kind of reward, then the wholly sacrificial approach of organisms in the natural world could be said to have motivations that were even more 'pure' than ours.

'Commerce, trade and exchange make other people more valuable alive than dead, and mean that people try to anticipate what the other guy needs and wants. It engages the mechanisms of reciprocal altruism, as the evolutionary biologists call it, as opposed to raw dominance.'
Stephen Pinker, *How The Mind Works*

Trivers, himself, wondered if: '... models that attempt to explain altruistic behaviour in terms of natural selection are models designed to take the altruism out of altruism?'

So, what did he think was the bottom line of it all? How did our human behaviour separate us out from the deal-making that takes place in Nature? In summary, he said, human altruism was an essentially unstable process that mixes emotions in with our highly developed ability to assess favours. It was what he believed lay behind the great forward momentum of our biological heritage.

His view was that our ancient genetic programming to find reciprocating organisms to help us - to be endlessly on the lookout for joint benefits in other words - had morphed in us humans through our cultural evolution to end up with our compassionate and moral intuitions. While many of the reasons we repay acts of kindness are based on sincerely meant instincts we are, nonetheless, always 'adding up the score' in our dealings.

He concluded that this constant balancing of our cooperation and defection tactics had given us the insights we need for what he listed out as: 'friendship, dislike, moralistic aggression, gratitude, sympathy, trust, suspicion, trustworthiness, aspects of guilt and some forms of dishonesty and hypocrisy.' If this list isn't what Stephen Pinker was to call '... the intricately complicated and endlessly fascinating relationships that bind us one to another', I don't know what is.

Why have we ended up like this? Trivers believes it's because we've spent so much of the long march of our cultural development living in small, stable groups that kept track of who owed what to whom, who was collaborating, who could be trusted and who was likely to cheat, why they were doing it, and what built or diminished communities.

The lessons we'd learnt from this long conditioning had bedded down into our neural programming over so many millennia that they're what formed the basis of our obsessions with fair division and justice. As Matt Ridley summarises it in *The Origins of Virtue*: 'Emotions elicit reciprocity in our species and they direct us towards altruism when it might, in the long run, pay. We like people who are altruistic towards us, and are altruistic towards people who like us.'

Robert Trivers' great contribution was to see that the iterated prisoner's dilemma - without an end game so there's no shadow of backward induction hanging over it - was what exposed the logic of reciprocal altruism. The longer that organisms interact, he said, the greater was the chance that cooperation would evolve between them.

The same is true of us humans. The more that people deal with each other, the higher is the likelihood that knowledge, trust and friendship will emerge, and that Always Cooperate will then lead to us having a stake in each other's lives. Two hundred years before Trivers' visionary insight, Adam Smith had said exactly the same thing. Both could see that cooperation was bound to emerge when this happened. The result was the process that produced trading, fair exchange and the growth of prosperity.

> '**Trivers has answered some of the most difficult questions about the human condition - why are our relationships with people such complicated mixtures of cooperation and conflict? He did so with a simple, non-obvious analysis of the patterns of overlap and nonoverlap of our long-term genetic interests.**'
> **Steven Pinker, *Enlightenment Now***

Yet again, game theory was illustrating that it's rational to be irrational - and that it's therefore logical to *trust* people. There are clearly benefits to be had if one can only do that. But, as Trivers' reciprocating mechanism shows, the problem remains that we have to expect that some people will exploit this by cheating. This is why we - and everything else in Nature - need to be able to identify wrongdoers and to have the ability to punish them. Without these defences, the defectors will multiply.

On the other hand, if we choose to keep playing 'Defect', we may be protecting ourselves from possible exploitation, but we're giving up the chance of long-term gains. The philosopher Amartya Sen summed up these sorts of people when he called them 'rational fools'. Don't know about you, but I seem to have come across quite a few in my life.

> 'Nature's stern discipline enjoins mutual help at least
> as often as warfare. The fittest may also be the gentlest.'
> Theodosius Dobzhansky, *Mankind Evolving:*
> *The Evolution of the Human Species*

But questions yet remained unanswered.

Was it possible, some biologists began to ask, that in the great thrashing ocean of organisms interacting, reciprocal altruism was the reason that things were held in balance? Could game theory explain that?

And if mutations kept cropping up, why didn't a few change living things in a way that would throw the whole balancing mechanism out... why didn't significant alterations occur more frequently in their behaviour? You'd think that if there were such constant changes coming through the gene pools of the natural world, then their vehicles, the organisms, would be constantly altering. So why did they remain unchanged for such long periods?

Perhaps even more baffling, why didn't a few things become so successful that they 'won' in life? Why hadn't organisms evolved to become so well adapted that they would keep beating everything else... and so last forever?

Well, someone was now going to make a return to the stage... and he was going to have a pretty good go at answering many of these nagging issues.

The world may be teeming with different organisms...
but every one of them is in an Evolutionary Stable State.

CHAPTER TEN

FROM THE EARLY 1970s, A NEW GENERATION OF BIOLOGISTS WAS INCREASINGLY LOOKING AT EVOLUTION FROM THE 'GENE'S EYE' POINT OF VIEW. HOWEVER, THE PROBLEM THIS GAVE THEM WAS THAT IF THE GENE WAS SO CLEVER ABOUT GETTING ITS VEHICLES TO 'WIN', WHY HADN'T MUTATIONS ARRIVED AT SOMETHING THAT TRIUMPHED OVER EVERYTHING ELSE?

Seen from a historical perspective, there can't have been many more exciting times to have been an evolutionary biologist than in the years after the Second World War.

The way that DNA replicated life forms fundamentally changed the thinking when it was discovered in the early 1950s. Then the ways the gene influenced which elements should be favourably selected for, and propagated, were pioneered in the 1960s.

Bill Hamilton then came from nowhere in 1964 to prove mathematically that evolution had made it worthwhile for things to sacrifice their lives if it meant their close relatives could pass on their genes. This could only mean that the gene was the great organiser of life. The American biologist, George Williams, would take on the argument that the gene was the master replicator, and that it only 'viewed' living things as ways of hedging its evolutionary bets. Organisms, he famously concluded, were just its temporary homes.

Robert Trivers went on to use the prisoner's dilemma in 1971 to solve the problem of why things would ever compromise their reproductive fitness for something else. Reciprocal altruism - back scratching as he described it - explained how the gene directed organisms to help each other if they mutually benefited, just as long as they could recognise and punish things if they cheated.

But now, as the Seventies unfolded, someone was going to rejoin the story who would answer quite a few of the remaining questions about how life sorted itself out on this strange planet of ours. This is going to be the second appearance in these books of John Maynard Smith. If you recall from Book One, he'd been working at UCL when he'd published a joint paper with George Price that put forward a ground-breaking rationale for the weird rituals of animal conflict.

Maynard Smith was originally a mathematician, and when Trivers' findings had first appeared, he'd set out to re-examine a number of his earlier game theoretic conclusions. Could they explain, he wondered, what lay behind some of the things that we take for granted in life, but which are nonetheless pretty bizarre?

In particular, why was it that if organisms were mutating all the time… then how come they didn't alter *faster*? If these random genetic accidents were so frequent, then surely a few of them would turn out to be such amazing improvements that they'd change the way a species looked and behaved? Why didn't innovations end up by shoving the old ways of existing out of the evolutionary road?

'Evolutionary game theorists hold that organisms compete over a source of objective fitness and that each organism's survival depends on gaining more than others.'
SM Amadae, *Prisoners of Reason*

Yet it was pretty obvious that the opposite occurred… organisms stayed the same for remarkably long periods. But why was that? Didn't it stand to reason that they were constantly in danger of extinction if something better came along to take over their cosy niches.

And what about the big question… the one the Guru had posed? If mutations were always popping up with potentially life changing breakthroughs, then why didn't something *win forever*? Why weren't the most successful organisms sitting at the top of the teeming mass of other life forms - and staying there because they'd evolved to have no weaknesses, no enemies and no threats? In other words, why hadn't evolution come up with something that was immortal?

Maynard Smith had thought that game theory could provide the answers. Like other evolutionary theorists of the time, he too had arrived at the conclusion that the gene was in some way influencing organisms to develop their behavioural decisions. And if the advances being made in game theory research did anything, he felt, they had the potential to explain how those choices were made. Researchers had spent years computer modelling human behaviour, and biologists were now beginning to argue that although things in the natural world might not have our ability to weigh up the evidence, it was nevertheless plain that successful decisions should *persist* in a species rather than keep changing.

The reason they were saying this was because the choices that were being made ultimately led to something's fitness. Fitter genes succeed because they have higher rates of reproduction. Organisms that are the fittest produce the greatest number of offspring. That's how it all works.

This logically meant, Maynard Smith would later explain, that the natural world didn't need to have our capacity for reason and self-interest to make their decisions, because in Nature: '… rationality is replaced by that of population dynamics and stability, and the criterion of self-interest, by Darwinian fitness.'

'Every form of behaviour is shaped by trial and error. Since the work of Maynard Smith and others, it has been realised how game theory can model this process. Evolutionary game theory replaces the static solutions of classical game theory by a dynamical approach centred not on the concept of rational players but on the population dynamics of behavioural programmes.'
Josef Hofbauer and Karl Sigmund, *Evolution, Games and Population Dynamics*

Now he took this as his start point and began to apply game theoretic reasoning to see how the gene's choices could end up with behavioural outcomes. In particular, he figured, if games offered an insight into how conflict and cooperation worked together, then surely the method an organism used to choose its behaviour would have a similar mechanism to the way humans picked a strategy that they thought would win a game.

Strategies, he could see, were encoded biologically and then inherited down the generations. Living things didn't have to be aware they were making decisions or playing games, but nonetheless their reproductive success - their fitness - was arrived at in exactly the same way that payoffs were in the prisoner's dilemma.

'As one moves up the evolutionary ladder in neural complexity, game playing behaviour becomes richer.'
Itai Yanai and Martin J Lercher, *Genome Biology*

The evolutionary theorist, Martin Nowak, describes in his autobiographical book, *SuperCooperators*, how Maynard Smith had his light bulb moment. He paints a picture of him sitting down one evening with a highly technical study of game theory and racking his brains to see if the mathematical logic had any relevance for his research. 'After a few pages', says Nowak, 'he decided to abandon the textbook and continue to develop his own thoughts.'

And it was at this point that he came up with the concept I described in Book One for what he was to call an 'evolutionary stable strategy'. It was this, he was to say, that would lead to things staying the same - because they'd be in what was termed an 'evolutionary stable state', or ESS.

An ESS, he said, meant that if there wasn't an ecological change that put a species' way of life in danger - something that suddenly pulled the rug out from under its way of living - then no variant of it could come along that would get more genes out into the next generation than the way the organism was already doing. In other words, it could never be 'invaded', even though something new might be *more* fit.

'In this way', Nowak continued, 'Maynard Smith stumbled across a way to play games with a population which was fundamental to thinking about evolution. What is remarkable is that if he had stuck to the textbook he would have found, a few pages later, the very (same) concept of the Nash Equilibrium.'

Ha. What Maynard Smith had arrived at was that just as two parties in a game - whether it was the Cold War's arms race, competitors in a market, or even a pair of squabbling partners - could use their judgements to see that even though they might be better off if they changed their strategies, the risk of being the first one to do this was just too great. The other might then take advantage of the cooperative initiative. This was how the Nash Equilibrium worked.

And it's why we humans, in spite of having information, communication, internal reasoning, experience and 'the shadow of the future' to help us arrive at our decisions, can still frequently end up in this state of affairs. Maynard Smith's great insight, however, was to realise that although other living things had none of our cognitive abilities, *everything in the natural world* had arrived at exactly the same equilibrium point.

Here, yet again, was the proof that the gene was acting almost as if it had an extraordinary intelligence. Yes, mutations might be welcome events if environmental change made life difficult for the vehicle that was carrying it around. But if outside influences remained unchanged, then no attempt by a genetic invader would ever be able to take over a population. Instead, given time, any new variants would eventually die off.

This was the process of natural selection laid bare. Reproductive success was acting in exactly the same way as the outcomes of the prisoner's dilemma.

In a nutshell, Maynard Smith was now concluding that this was why living things stayed the same. It didn't matter what an invader might do, because the original organism *would reply in kind*. Maynard Smith called it 'like begets like'... because whatever was thrown at it would be met in return, and sometimes even copied if it led to an advantage.

This meant that things were bound to evolve to the point where they were evolutionarily 'stable'. They'd then have the defence mechanisms to reject any harmful mutational innovations trying to muscle in. This was the way that things would remain unchanged and in an equilibrium - until environmental conditions went against them. If that happened, then they'd need mutations to get around the problems - or the species would become extinct. Suddenly, in other words, the invading strategy might be welcomed and used.

It was this inight that led Maynard Smith and George Price to their view that organisms often arrived at their evolutionary strategy by using various methods of *internal competition* (like the stag contests) to make sure that their genes had perfected how they were going to live.

In other words, the 'mutations versus the existing organism' activities were endlessly checking that no new strategy would succeed. Equally, these challenges were keeping the organism at peak fitness because 'like was begetting like' and any

The hawk and dove playing their
parts in the balance of nature.

useful improvements were incorporated. This was what convinced Maynard Smith and Price that Hamilton's view was vindicated, and that these conflicts were originating at the level of the gene.

But how did organisms make sure that things always turned out right?

The answers to this issue arose in exactly the same way that the iterated prisoner's dilemma illustrates the interaction of conflict and cooperation. Organisms arrive at the same point that humans do when we're dealing with each other, in that they're playing their invasion and defence strategies by responding to what the other one was doing.

Thomas Vincent and Joel Brown beautifully summed up this process in *Evolutionary Game Theory* when they wrote: 'The players are the individual organisms. Strategies are heritable phenotypes. A player's strategy set is the set of all evolutionarily feasible strategies. Payoffs in the evolutionary game are expressed in terms of fitness.'

In this sense, using the Dilemma to look at how biological processes work is no different to the way that it's used to explain our own interactions. And just as social scientists had used the image of Hawks and Doves to describe how conflicts in human populations evolve to produce cooperation, so Maynard Smith was now saying exactly the same thing about the evolutionary process of organisms. As with humans, he said, choosing to 'Defect' is a zero sum, Hawkish strategy, and choosing to 'Cooperate' is a non-zero, Dovish one.

So say there's a population of animals competing over a resource, like food. If every individual behaves like a Dove and shares it out fairly, then the colony is acting in the same way that humans do in a trusting, compassionate society that's playing Always Cooperate. But this makes the community vulnerable to attack by invading Hawks who want to grab the food and ignore the needs of others.

What happens, however, if there's a mix of Hawks and Doves in the colony? Because the Hawks' aggression easily reduces the Doves to small numbers, this increases the proportion of Hawks.

Of course they then maul each other because this is how their brains are coded and they're incapable of cooperation. In the numerical terms of the Dilemma, they finish up with very few points. This is why they reduce their numbers… at which point Retaliator Doves come to the fore.

They then expand their presence by finding others like themselves to deal with -

sharing food out more fairly in this example. And, by doing this, it means that their presence in the population grows, and this restores Dovish cooperation to the system.

What Maynard Smith managed to arrive at was the mathematical proof that the Always Defect strategy wasn't any more evolutionarily stable than the Always Cooperate one was. (Not that strange really, when you think about our own lives. After all, how often do you see societies made up only of unremitting bastards? Or ones entirely consisting of Pollyannas?) A mixture of strategies was stable, he said.

And just as humans hop around between zero sum and non-zero strategies when we interact with other people, so does everything else in Nature. However, because there are many players in a population, and not just the two that game theory's research usually uses, the end result is that there are bound to be colossal numbers of potential tactics at play - and mutations are constantly stirring the pot by introducing new ones.

An evolutionary stable state, therefore, was one that had been challenged by countless alternative strategies… and had survived.

What does this all mean? Well, setting the bewildering mathematical modelling to one side, the underlying conclusion Maynard Smith had come to was to show how the mechanics of natural selection operate in evolution. Conflicts might be the external signs of it, he said, but actually the organism is continuously testing itself at the genetic level.

Maynard Smith was to wrap up his convictions in a 1982 book called *Evolution and the Theory of Games*. In this he concluded that the presence of evolutionary stable strategies throughout the natural world had made it possible to explain the basis for three of the most evident, and yet elusive phenomena in the history of life on earth.

First, he said, the fact that there was a genetic rationale for every species being in an evolutionary stable state now shone a light on why species maintain their appearance, abilities and behaviour. Their internal processes kept things at peak fitness, he said, and they would stay that way unless an environmental shift meant that mutations might suddenly be beneficial for the vehicle's, and the gene's, survival.

'Although evolution may seem, in some vague sense, a 'good thing',
especially since we are the product of it, nothing actually 'wants' to evolve.'
Richard Dawkins, *The Selfish Gene*

Secondly, the role an evolutionary strategy plays in a species' stability explains why organisms don't move about on the Behavioural Spectrum. It was now clear that once they'd found a position that suited them - something that provided them with a niche they could survive in - then they don't make the kind of hopping around in their behaviour that we humans do. They don't change because these niches aren't empty spaces that are waiting to be filled, but hard won arrangements that help an organism overcome the threat of entropic forces.

But, thirdly was his belief that *the vivid interplay of Hawks and Doves is the explanation for the balance of Nature.* That's because everything in life, from microbial colonies right up to to the largest of animals, and from the smallest of brains up to us sentient humans (and John von Neumann beyond us), are all faced by the same threat of zero sum, aggressive members of their communities trying to beat everything around them. They do this because they're genetically programmed to only play Defect. In short, to be Hawks.

Yet game theory had, as Maynard Smith was to write: '… paradoxically turned out to be more readily applied to biology than the field of economic behaviour for which it was originally designed.' And he'd used it to show how there was an endless process going on of new approaches trying to find weaknesses in organisms - and then trying to exploit them when they did so.

'(In non humans)… the criterion of rationality is replaced by that of population
dynamics and stability, and the criterion of self-interest by Darwinian fitness.'
John Maynard Smith, *Evolution and the Theory of Games*

This means that right throughout each level of complexity in the natural world, every single thing is constantly being challenged.

Even at the microbial level, the heaving superstew of bacteria and viruses are always fighting out their Hawks and Doves games. Within every life form, new strategies are constantly coming along, searching for any cracks in the armour of different species, finding out whether their behaviour and phenotypes are truly stable, and therefore operating at peak fitness.

The same process is happening at all times and in all species, as the ying of competitive actions is set against the yang of the cooperative gains available from symbioses and reciprocal altruism.

'Evolutionary game theory is a way of thinking about evolution
at the phenotypic level when the fitness of particular phenotypes

The Secrets of Life - Book Three

In summary, every organism is being threatened by something else - either internally or externally. And game theory shows how *mixed strategies* are being employed in the natural world every bit as much as they are in our human societies.

The result? Over the long history of life on earth, the two strategies have kept the billions and billions of species 'in balance'. Of course, there are lurches to this stability when sudden ecological change comes along, the most obvious of which is a mass extinction. But the game theoretic conclusions are always the same... that an equilibrium is restored once organisms settle down to regular interaction, beneficial ecological arrangements, synergies and reciprocal altruism.

What game theory had made clear was that organisms who use the strategy of zero sum domination might reduce populations that rely on working together. But they'll always fail to win in the long run. That's because, over evolutionary time, cooperative strategies will claw back the *collective points* available to non-zero players, and the gains that come from collaborating will inevitably overcome selfish opponents.

But if cooperation really is the victor, this was all sounding a long way from the top-down language that describes Nature as being 'red in tooth and claw'. Most of us are brought up to believe that Darwinism suggests that only the strong survive the 'struggle for existence'. Were the world's biologists now seeing things differently?

And what did this all mean for us humans?

'How was the reception to my book? Well, it seems a couple of people might have taken a few things the wrong way.'

BY THE 1970s THE GENE-BASED THEORY OF EVOLUTION WAS BEING VIEWED AS MORE THAN JUST AN INTERESTING NEW WAY OF LOOKING AT LIFE. UNDERSTANDING THE ROLE THAT ALTRUISM PLAYED HAD BECOME THE KEY TO SEEING THE GENE AS THE CONDUCTOR OF LIFE'S ORCHESTRA, AND ORGANISMS AS SIMPLY THE INSTRUMENTS. BUT WHO, AND WHAT, WAS GOING TO TURN THIS INSIGHT INTO MAINSTREAM THINKING?

Looking back on things, some people now see JBS Haldane as having a claim on the idea of putting the gene at the centre of evolutionary theory, when he made his boozy observation about brothers and cousins back in 1955.

Again, in retrospect, Bill Hamilton's exposure in 1964 of how eusocial insects acted for the sake of their genes, and then the research work done by George Williams, can both now be seen as making major advances. Williams published his findings in a hugely influential book called *Adaptation and Natural Selection* in 1966 and, in academic circles, the gene-centred theory was getting a lot of purchase by the time the decade was coming to an end.

Nonetheless, it was all still widely regarded as fringe thinking. You might have thought, for instance, that Hamilton's extraordinary insights about the purpose of sacrifice in sterile organisms would have triggered a tsunami of interest from other biologists. Yet oddly enough, not a single citation of his papers had appeared even a decade later. This seems bizarre given that social insects were well known for having arrived at an incredibly successful strategy, and yet theories about how they lived and worked for each other had only ever been based on assumptions.

Everything changed once Bill Hamilton's work became more widely accepted. John Maynard Smith was later to describe him, and his place in evolutionary thinking, as 'the only bloody genius we've got'. Richard Dawkins, too, was in no doubt about his contribution to genetic theory when he picked him as his choice for the BBC's *Great Lives* series. Looking back at the role he'd played in exposing the reasons for altruistic behaviour, he summed Hamilton up as having given the world: '… a Darwinian basis for… sympathy, empathy and our desire to help and cooperate with others.'

But if these men had opened up the first cracks in the walls of previous theories, the fissures were to widen enormously when the appearance of Robert Trivers' papers, and then John Maynard Smith's theories, catalysed an entire rethink of evolutionary theory. Now they, and a growing number of their followers, were bringing out game theoretic solutions that gave weight to views that had remained largely unchallenged since Fisher's day.

Before their collective insights came along, the mystery of altruism - why one organism would sacrifice its fitness to enhance that of another - was so contrary to the long-accepted idea of evolution that the phenomenon was regarded as contrary to the whole concept of 'Darwinism'. In fact, the only explanation for it had been that weird behaviour like this somehow stemmed from the survival drives of the *group*, and meant that individual organisms were carrying out these acts for the good of their species - the hive, the pack, the nest or whatever. What helped the group, in short, was then being beneficially transmitted down into its individual members' genes - rather than the other way around.

The two different theories now became locked in a scientific arm wrestle. It looked as if the traditionalists might hold their own until a couple of blockbusters hit the book stands in the mid 1970s that decisively tipped the scales in favour of the gene-based beliefs.

Both of them were examples of a new kind of science book: ones that were written by highly acclaimed academics but who were aiming at two quite separate audiences - their own scientific communities, and also the general reader. Taken together, they were going to arouse massive controversy, and ultimately to position evolutionary theory in the very heartland of people's ideas about human psychology, philosophy and social science.

The first to appear was *Sociobiology: The New Synthesis*. This was the magnum opus of EO Wilson, the distinguished Harvard biologist, and in it he argued that social behaviour - where organisms were on the Behavioural Spectrum - was the result of the gene's role in the evolutionary forces that had formed them.

In particular, the support Wilson gave to his friend Bill Hamilton's explanation of how inclusive fitness - kin selection - led to altruism in eusocial insects was a huge stamp of approval for the new thinking. In turn the book's reception heaped praise on Wilson's exploration of the ways in which genetic evolution had led organisms to adopt behaviours such as territorial conflicts, pack hunting and mate selection.

But if many in the biological community recognised the book's contribution to evolutionary theory... pretty well everyone else began to freak out. This was because Wilson had included humans in his worldview of genetic history. We were all part of the same story, in there along with every other species, and this made us, he said, simply the end products of a chain of biological logic.

Woah. In particular, what got a lot of people frothed up was his final chapter - rather provocatively headed 'Man' - in which he seemed to be implying support for the idea of genetic determinism. The clear inference was that we were the products of our animal inheritance, and that human actions and power structures were therefore due to the influence of our genes. Our behaviour was driven by these influences, he said, and this led to our views on such critical issues as sexuality, hierarchies, class differences, traits, personal abilities and tribalism.

What we'd evolved to become, in short, had largely been dictated by our genes, and had through natural selection. This could only mean, as one of his critics said at the time: 'that human ethics and morality should be expressed biologically rather than philosophically.'

> **'Despite its noble purpose and history, pure philosophy long**
> **ago abandoned the foundational questions about human existence.'**
> EO Wilson, *The Social Conquest of Earth*

At this point the balloon went up. What could Wilson mean other than that he was undermining human intellect, morality and dignity? At the very least, the man was being an irresponsible social threat. The debate looked as if it would rumble on in the usual pattern when a well-known academic proposes a radical explanation, but instead of dying down, the argument went nuclear when a deeply unpleasant review appeared on the front page of the *New York Times*. This might have made less of a splash if it hadn't been written by a pair of Wilson's own Harvard colleagues, the Marxist biologists Stephen Jay Gould and Richard Lewontin.

These two now suggested that the 'new' science of sociobiology had nasty, right wing overtones. They accused Wilson of proposing that human nature - our psychology and social behaviour - was inescapably tied to our genetic inheritance, and that he was being absolutist about the very foundation of human behaviour. The result? Well, it was hardly surprising that the increasingly sensitive political atmosphere of the mid-Seventies seized on the row, garnished it with a few of the other hot issues of the day, and a stream of denouncements quickly followed.

Free will? Compassion? Love? Respect? The idea of humans having higher qualities than other animals? That was all rubbish, objectors claimed Wilson to be saying. Out came the placards and slogans, protest marches were organised wherever he went to lecture, and 'right thinking people' were up in arms.

It didn't help that he was a very high-profile prey. As the acknowledged world authority on the subject, he was bound to be in the firing line if he was putting forward arguments that horrible traits such as aggressiveness, sexism, racism, authoritarianism and totalitarianism came from our biological inheritance rather than from our social development. Nazis, his critics believed him to be saying, were neither wrong nor right… they were just understandable human versions of our predator pasts.

Wilson was by repute a warm, courteous man with the thoughtful manners of the Old South, but he refused to take this lying down. He quickly began to fight back by stressing that humans were far more fluid in their social organisation than other organisms, and were therefore able to reason through to how they interacted. Their choices of behaviour, he said, were the result of cultural evolution as well as genetic.

But people weren't listening too closely by now. Whatever he was saying, they weren't hearing - and it became widely believed that what he really meant was that any conflict between 'nature and nurture' was very largely a myth.

Was this treatment entirely unfair? Well, poor Wilson never actually spelt out that he thought human feelings and actions were determined by our DNA, but a large number of readers nonetheless assumed that's what he meant. And he didn't help himself when he was later quoted as saying, rather bizarrely, that only '10% of our behaviour' was due to our cultural history.

'Scientists and humanists should consider the possibility that the time has come for ethics to be removed temporarily from the hands of philosophers and biologized.'
EO Wilson, *Sociobiology*

Wilson's overriding contention was that comparing ourselves to other organisms and species was helpful, and that like them, our genes and experiences had travelled down through the generations. However, he stopped well short of saying that genes actually *controlled* our behaviour. Rather, he said, their contribution had to be *added to* our cultural inheritance and shared experiences, and it was for these reasons that he subscribed to the growing popularity of the phrase 'gene-culture co-evolution'. Nice try, but he still spent many years fighting uphill against the appalled responses

The Oxford spires where Dawkins' dreams
about selfish genes took hold.

of people who wouldn't be talked out of believing he was advocating repressive social policies.

Naturally, a great deal of the academic rancour eventually died down, and with more considered views came a general acceptance of the importance of the gene, and the less inflammatory rebranding of sociobiology as 'evolutionary psychology'.

As time passed he was to become widely regarded as one of the grand old men of evolutionary theory. This persisted even though he was later to change his mind on the mechanism for altruism, something that, sadly, led to him being consigned to the pile of suspects that are pilloried for still supporting 'group selection' theory.

If *Sociobiology* was the first barrel to be fired from the new evolutionary theory shotgun, the other came a few months later from Richard Dawkins, then a young Oxford academic. His extraordinary book was called *The Selfish Gene*, and it caught mainstream attention as a beautifully written treatise that distilled the new biological thinking into one place, and then added some genius level insights from his own research. It was, he said, an attempt to present the case for 'the biology of selfishness and altruism'.

Robert Trivers contributed a powerful Foreword, and the book became an immediate megahit. First published in 1976, it's been in print ever since, translated into twenty-five languages and selling over a million copies. A scientific breakthrough it may have been, yet the ideas in it were put forward in such an easy and approachable style that even dimwits like me were able to understand them.

The Selfish Gene was the result of convictions that had been growing in Dawkins for well over a decade. He described their origin in his autobiography, *An Appetite for Wonder*, when he related how he was working as a research assistant for the Nobel Laureate, Nino Tinbergen. This led to him being asked, one day, to stand in for his boss and deliver a lecture to a group of students.

Dawkins' notes for his talk could have been written yesterday. In them he sums up his enduring views: 'Genes are, in a sense, immortal… Natural selection will favour those genes which build themselves into a body which is most likely to succeed in handing down safely to the next generation a large number of replicas of those genes… our basic expectation on the basis of the orthodox, neo-Darwinian theory of evolution, therefore, is that genes will be *selfish*.'

This was an extraordinary encapsulation of the new thinking. The organism, he was saying, didn't lead in the dance for survival; instead, it was the gene itself that was in charge, single-minded and utterly focussed on doing its job. And its job, its whole purpose, was to somehow *find a way of keeping life going*.

If that aim was being carried out by a particular organism then great, the gene would do everything it could to help that life form survive. If not, then sayonara sucker. The gene wasn't going to shed any tears for the loser - it would be too busy trying to find something else to support. And if 99.9% of all the species that have ever lived really have become extinct, then there must have been quite a few goodbyes along the way.

Was this 'selfish' behaviour? Yes, in one sense, because the gene was never going to put all its efforts behind any single organism. It wasn't going to have its bets on just one horse, it was going to own the racecourse. And, yes, if it meant that the gene would discard an organism for another that had a better chance of helping life survive, and keeping entropy at bay, then again, guilty as charged.

But on the other hand, no, Dawkins wasn't saying that this genetic vector was leading *organisms* to be selfish, let alone that the gene itself was motivated by human desires like glory or willpower. It might look as if it was because it was focussed on survival to the exclusion of everything else… but it had no morals or ethical judgement.

Dawkins himself, apparently, was to sometimes regret that he didn't follow his publisher's advice that the word 'immortal' might be more explanatory and less inflammatory than 'selfish'. But personally, I'm not so sure… 'selfish' seems to me to completely encapsulate its blinkered focus, and the fact that organisms themselves are not responsible for the entirety of their evolutionary mechanisms.

In many ways, being selfish is the last thing that genes are. Instead, they show themselves to be so dedicated to doing their job that they even direct some of their vehicles to sacrifice themselves so that others like themselves might live. As to his own position on the description, Dawkins made it clear that: '… the definitions of altruism and selfishness are behavioural not subjective (and) concerned only with whether the effect of an act is to lower or raise the prospects of the presumed altruist and the survival prospects of the presumed beneficiary.'

Successful genes, he was saying, will help a species' chances. And if this species does well, then great - the genes will spread. In short, the relationship between the gene and the organism is the ultimate symbiosis in life.

The geneticist, Adam Rutherford, was later to write that the book, and Dawkins himself, were: '… bridges, both intellectually and chronologically between the titans of mid-century biology - Fisher, Trivers, Hamilton, Maynard Smith and Williams - and our era of the genome, in which the interrogation of DNA dominates the study of evolution.'

Among other breakthroughs described in *The Selfish Gene*, Dawkins examined the evidence for cooperation, 'the biology of selfishness and altruism', of kin selection, and of how this proves that the gene is the 'replicator' in the reproduction process - and not the organism.

**'It requires a deliberate mental effort to turn biology the right way up again,
and remind ourselves that the replicators come first, in importance as well as history.'
Richard Dawkins, *The Selfish Gene***

He explains how this process works within living things to produce phenotypes, and why these end up being so beautifully designed for the environment. He also covers how these then reach out into the world in the form of 'extended phenotypes' like nests and dams; how all organisms search for an ESS, how populations produce evolutionary stability, and how in simple terms, natural selection comes about.

But like Wilson, he writes about us humans too, and about how we've inherited all the extraordinary biological beauty that evolution creates. Of course, he acknowledges, we're the product of our genetic inheritance because we're made of the same material as everything else and our genes are trying to achieve the same survival result.

Having accepted this biological background, Dawkins then goes on to explain how we've layered on top of this heritage the accretion of all the things that have shaped us, coming as they have from the cascade of revolutions that contributed to our cultural development.

To do this he shows how 'memes' - a word he invented to describe units of information - act like genes in being passed down between us vertically, through inheritance. But, he says, they also travel horizontally by means of our human interaction. These memes are part of how we copy and sculpt each other.

And it's because of our unique fusing of genetic and cultural factors, he concludes, that we've ended up as the first species in the world's history to have the capacity *not* to be ruled by the instructions of our genes. Instead, we can take our own productive and inventive steps to override the orders we're receiving from them… even though we frequently find that this can be dangerous, painful or downright confusing.

> **'When thinking about cultural evolution, don't get wrapped up in the ways of any particular people. Instead, keep your eyes on the memes. People come and go but memes, like genes, persist. They pass on and influence what happens next'**
> **Robert Wright, *Nonzero***

The Selfish Gene became a landmark. It was from its appearance onwards really, that the gene-based theory of evolution wasn't just a quirky adjunct to mainstream beliefs, but an entire and coherent explanation in itself.

Game theory had played a major part in this new understanding. It showed how there was a mathematical logic to the role cooperation played in overcoming the gloomy predictions of the 2nd Law of Thermodynamics. Ecological niches, Dawkins said, weren't just sitting there empty, waiting for things to fill them. They were created by organisms adapting themselves to the environments around them, in competition with - and sometimes by forming alliances with - other life forms that were also trying to maximise their chances of staying alive.

> **'(The prisoner's dilemma) exposes the workings of behaviour just as much as investigating the gradual changes that lead to evolution.'**
> **Matt Ridley, *The Origins of Virtue***

To do this, living things had to succeed, fight their corners and to win in the great game of life. But how, exactly? Yes, Rutherford's 'titans' had explored the interactions of conflict and cooperation - but how did these actually come about? How did cooperation ever get going if things were so concerned with looking after their own interests that they would never risk dealing with outsiders?

And even if they did, how would they make sure they came out on top? When these questions are applied to us humans, we have a ready answer for why we're so reluctant to take risks when it comes to trusting others because none of us would ever want to trade with someone else if they thought they were going to lose out or be continually beaten. And it had to make equal sense to assume that the other person, or organism, wouldn't want to lose out either.

So, how could one make sure of *winning*?

The great breakthroughs in evolutionary thinking had come from seeing how game theoretic results had answered these basic questions. The formalisation of the prisoner's dilemma had only arrived some two decades before, yet this 'silly game' had allowed mathematicians to see what succeeded in life, and why. Its applications had journeyed from economic theory to the arms race, then on to commercial negotiations and, lastly, to biology.

Now the story was going to come full circle - not only back to the US where it had originated… but also back to the social sciences.

What were researchers hoping to find? Well, the search for symbiotic collaboration and alliances had shown how advantageous they'd always been in evolution. But now the big questions were around the degree to which these same forces operated in us humans.

How, for example, did they influence the centuries-old tussles around the social contract - the balance between what was good for the individual and what was good for the group? Arguing about this had kept people in heated discussion for centuries, banging the supper table and shouting for more wine. But loud words and angry gestures had never managed to bottom out a solution.

So, could the circle ever be squared? Was it possible that when computer programmes were exploring the cold, mathematical logic of the Dilemma they would, at last, provide a mechanism for some kind of empirical evidence on the issue?

'Bill Hamilton around 1973. Robert Trivers said of him: 'He had the most subtle, multi-layered mind I have ever encountered. What he said often had double and even triple meanings so that, while the rest of us speak and think in single notes, he thought in chords.' Matt Ridley would later add that he erected '... an edifice of ideas stranger, more original and more profound than that of any other biologist since Darwin."

CHAPTER TWELVE

TRIVERS HAD SHOWN THAT RECIPROCAL ALLIANCES WITHIN - AND BETWEEN - SPECIES WERE UNQUESTIONABLY SUCCESSFUL STRATEGIES FOR THE GENE. BUT HOW WAS COOPERATION EVER TO TAKE ROOT IN A WORLD OF WIDESPREAD SUSPICION AND CONFLICT? WAS THERE A WAY FOR COLLABORATIVE BEHAVIOUR TO EVOLVE? EVEN TO WIN?

This is where the story takes a strange twist of coincidence.

By 1978, Bill Hamilton's breakthrough thinking on kin selection and the role of the gene had made it far better appreciated, largely due to Wilson's and Dawkins' books. His teaching and research abilities had always been in great demand, and the modest introvert was now approached by the University of Michigan to cross the Atlantic and accept the chair in Evolutionary Biology. He embraced his new life with enthusiasm, but he'd hardly stretched his long legs under a desk there before a young superstar social scientist called Robert Axelrod came by to introduce himself. Hamilton was intrigued to meet him as he'd heard a lot about his investigations into the behavioural logic that game theory was continuing to expose.

Axelrod was a fascinating man, a Chicago native who'd taken his doctorate in mathematics from Yale, and had then gone on to teach at Berkeley. Swathed in honours and prizes he was now back in the Midwest where, at the age of only thirty-one, he'd joined the staff at Michigan as the Professor of Political Science and Public Policy. He was widely recognised as a specialist in the area of conflict of interest and he was, like Hamilton, focused on the potential for mathematical analyses to shine a light on how our human fears and desires interacted.

This search had led to him becoming one of the boffins who were spending so many happy hours computer modelling the iterated prisoner's dilemma. By now there was a flourishing global community of people doing this, and all of them were trying to chase down the idea that there was a 'right' way to play. Their conviction was that if someone could only find the key, a door would open to reveal not only how living things achieved their optimal outcomes but, more importantly, what the mechanisms for natural selection were. Interrogating the game in this way was to illuminate what Stephen Pinker would later call a 'virtual evolutionary struggle'.

The question that badgered away at Axelrod, every bit as much as it had baffled so many other investigators, was to become the opening line of the book he would later write. This was called *The Evolution of Cooperation*, and it would soon become the standard work on the interaction of zero sum and non-zero drives. The question he set himself was this:

'Under what conditions will cooperation emerge in a world of egoists without central authority?'

Ha. What spin there is on that delivery. On the one hand, everyone would accept that collaboration is beneficial - because it leads to mutual gains. But on the other, our genetic and cultural motivations are Darwinian in that we're programmed to look out for ourselves. So how is it possible to achieve the right balance?

Hobbes had said that a 'terrour', a vengeful Leviathan, was needed to keep order, Locke thought a supreme authority was the way, ideally a king. Rousseau argued for some kind of democratic approval system; for Marx it was the workers' representatives, and for Lenin the Party.

But Adam Smith had asserted that *nobody* was needed, and that peace and cooperation would naturally evolve if people were able to trade with one another. It would flourish, he said, if communities were protected by good laws and regulations, had access to accurate and trusted information and their efforts were accelerated by the benefits of efficient transport.

All of these giants were brilliant men, thinkers who'd spent years racking their brains for the right solutions. If they couldn't agree, then how could ordinary people ever decide on what was the best guide to arrive at an orderly, productive society? Now Axelrod was convinced that game theory could get to the bottom of this swampy philosophical marshland. But how? And then he had a brainwave.

Still back in the days before emails, he sent out letters to the world's most noted researchers into the iterated prisoner's dilemma. In them he said that he was organising a *competition* to see which strategy would achieve the most points over a long period of repeated games. Everyone loves a competition. Everyone was convinced they knew the right way to play... and everyone had a pet theory about how to *win*.

And so he put together a tournament in which the entries he got back entered into a round robin, rather like a golf club ladder. In this way they'd fight it out with each other - and with itself by also putting in a twin of its own strategy. Last, Axelrod himself designed a programme that would make purely random choices so that Cooperate and Defect were played with equal probability.

Fourteen different programmes came in from game theorists and were fed into the university's sausage machine. Axelrod's 'Random' made it fifteen. He then set the computer simulations to slog it out over 200 games of the Dilemma - and the winner would be the one with the most points. In all 240,000 choices were going to be explored within 120,000 different games. Why did he pick 200 games? Because he figured that this would give a long enough series to see what happened over a realistic period, and yet it also gave him the opportunity to discount the backward induction effect by chopping out the last few plays if he had to.

What won? Well, almost incredibly, it was the shortest entry. Just four lines of computer code that had arrived from a Ukrainian-born concert pianist named Anatol Rapoport. Rapoport was an interesting man who'd switched careers from music to mathematics when he'd first arrived in the US, and had then risen in academia to spend many years as a Professor of Mathematical Biology at, oddly enough, the University of Michigan. But he'd then moved on to concentrate on the rather more saintly work of promoting world peace. He was now living in Toronto where he was the Professor Emeritus in Mathematics and Psychology. If ever there was a person who seemed completely qualified to show how cooperation could triumph, it was to be him.

Rapoport's entry was to become folklore among game theorists. Surprisingly, it was also going to lead philosophers and religious leaders to utter long sighs of... 'oh, how wonderful.'

His programme spelt out this simple strategy:

Never be the first to Defect. If you play first, then open with Cooperate. After that, repeat whatever the other player does.

It was as easy to understand as that. Axelrod immediately called it Tit for Tat.

So, say you have the opening choice in a new relationship... what Rapoport's strategy dictated was for you to start by *trusting* the other person. You'd therefore open with Cooperate. If the other player trusts in return, then he'll play Cooperate - and you'll also then reply with this again. If both of you keep going like this, then you'll be racking up six points between you. It was the polar opposite of the prisoners in their cells. What was logical in an iterated Dilemma would have been illogical in a one-time game.

However, if the other person went first and had opened with Defect - or if he betrays you by suddenly switching from Cooperate to Defect in mid game (so snatching five points instead of three) - then you immediately move to playing Defect instead. If he then holds out an olive branch and shifts back from Defect to Cooperate, you should instantly follow his lead and revert to Cooperate yourself. It couldn't have been simpler... and it couldn't have been more successful.

What? Isn't that crazy? Everyone knows that it's the strong that win in life, not cooperative types. Surely the tough guys always push the weeds out of the way? But now Rapoport's approach seemed to be showing that the best way of accumulating points was to keep playing Cooperate - as long as the other fellow did. This seemed to be the complete reversal of what one might have thought. Yet it swept all the other entries before it... but could this really be true?

No doubt the news they'd been beaten by such an absurdly childish approach didn't go down too well with the massed ranks of the world's eggheads. Not only would they have been offended by the strategy's simplicity, but it just didn't seem to make any sense. Why wasn't a more ruthless approach smashing the opposition? The winning entry was now suggesting that cooperation succeeded... something must have gone wrong.

And so Axelrod set about organising another tournament - this time with the express intention of putting Tit for Tat in its place.

The news of the second round quickly got about, and this time sixty-two entries from seven different countries were lined up as challengers. Some came in from hobbyists, determined to show the big boys that common sense would prevail. Some were from evolutionary biologists, some from physicists, and yet others from social scientists. No doubt everyone had been stung by Tit for Tat's apparent lack of sophistication. Surely their elaborately brilliant programmes would highlight its weaknesses this time?

Maynard Smith, as inventive and kindly as ever, put in a variant of Rapoport's idea. His approach had a twist that was designed to forgive a defection, because he reasoned that a player's choice might have been unintended, or a mistake that arose from a 'trembling hand'. Sadly his entry, Tit for Two Tats, was to be soundly beaten.

Robert Axelrod and Anatol Rapoport (right)... the creator of
possibly the cleverest four lines of code ever.

Anatol Rapoport crossed his arms as his strategy went into the new tournament unchanged... and the world's massed IQs threw their pet ideas at it time after time. And never laid a glove on him. The bodies of the losers piled up until the referee stepped in to declare Tit for Tat the undisputed winner. All that was now required was for the press to come up with their match reports to explain the reasons for its success.

Axelrod himself was in no doubt that his competition had revealed some extraordinary insights. Above all, it had shown that instead of having a secret strategy, being open and obvious in the way one played was key. It also showed that all those clichés that had been endlessly banged into us about how awful everyone was in life were simply wrong.

Tit for Tat's abiding lesson was that if one immediately trusted a stranger, then there was a good chance of being trusted in return. The unbending logic of the computer had shown that playing Cooperate wasn't just some kind of soppy instinct (possibly in the way that some had interpreted the Alchian-Williams experiments) but a cold, mathematical method of getting the most points.

'Although it seems paradoxical, 'altruistic' behaviour can emerge
as a direct consequence of the 'selfish' motives of a rational player.'
Martin Nowak, *SuperCooperators*

In human terms, the tactic was astute in that while the approach might be friendly, it could still immediately punish the other person if he didn't reciprocate. It wasn't being gooey. It was just seeking the most points, and it could sting as well as well as offer a helping hand. The downside was limited in other words, but the upside was limitless - because if cooperation set in then the two players could go on playing Tit for Tat until it became Always Cooperate, with each party sharing the six points.

In a competition that had set out to find the best way of playing, it was now plain that Tit for Tat wasn't so much a strategy as an invitation to become a trusted partner. Play my way, it was saying, and we can either fall out - or we can each keep cooperating, and continuously share in the six points that are on offer.

Axelrod realised that Rapoport's entry had exposed a profound evolutionary insight. The more he looked at how Tit for Tat worked, the more he could see that it had revealed the way for: '… a potentially cooperative strategy to get an initial foothold in an environment which is predominantly uncooperative.' This happened, he said, even when it was up against sophisticated opposition that already knew how Tit for Tat would behave.

In short, it was obvious that if the approach was extended out from a two-person game and became established within a community - even if people were using a wide variety of mixed strategies - it would not only win over the long run but it was also able to resist '… invasion by a less cooperative strategy'. It was like a beneficial virus in that it expanded, grew, and cooperation evolved.

The story now has a satisfying conclusion. Realising how Tit for Tat would *increase* in a group the longer that the individuals in it dealt with each other, Axelrod took the implications for human societies back into the field of biology… and shared his conclusions with Bill Hamilton. The two of them put their heads together. What they could see was that even though the tournament might have been conducted with human participants, the results had to have a universal application.

Tit for Tat was an exact parallel of the description Robert Trivers employed for 'reciprocal altruism'. Just as he'd proposed, altruistic behaviour could emerge as the rational outcome of a self-interested strategy. It won by letting the other side win as well. If this approach were followed, then it would end up with organisms playing Always Cooperate because they'd be continuously reciprocating. Trivers' logic had to be right, because this reciprocity could arise between unrelated partners if they were able to *recognise each other* - and could therefore establish trust between them. But this didn't mean they had to give up the capacity to punish defections. If something suddenly cheated, then the deal was over and the wrongdoer was identified.

Tit for Tat was also another way of describing Maynard Smith's 'like begets like'. Once he'd realised this was the case, Axelrod wrote his own definition of an evolutionary stable state, an ESS, as occurring within his tournaments when: '… no single differing mutant strategy can do better than others when the population is using this strategy.'

In short, Axelrod and Hamilton could see that the way humans played, even with all their intelligence and ability to imagine the consequences of their choices, was simply following the behavioural patterns of every other organism. As Matt Ridley was to sum it up in *The Origins of Virtue*: 'Natural selection, the driving force of evolution, is easily simulated on a computer: software creatures compete for space on the computer's screen in just the way that real creatures breed and compete for space in the real world.'

> 'I agree with Axelrod and Hamilton that many wild animals and plants are engaged in ceaseless games of the prisoner's dilemma, played out in evolutionary time.'
> **Richard Dawkins, *The Selfish Gene***

Working together, Bill Hamilton and Robert Axelrod set about producing a paper in March 1981 that was to be published in *Science* journal as *The Evolution of Cooperation*. Three years later Axelrod went on to expand their findings into a book with the same title. This was to become a landmark in game theorists' understanding of those strange intersections in which conflict collides with cooperation, and where the individual's interests are set against those of the group. What Axelrod had shown was that if one wanted to create equitable social contracts… then everything came back to the same mechanism of Tit for Tat.

Among other insights, the competition had reinforced the old finding that while it was understandable not to trust another person in a one-time prisoner's dilemma - where there's no opportunity to later punish a defection – this wasn't a factor when it's repeated over a lengthy period. When that's the case, the shadow of the future comes into its own. One is now able to see that playing Cooperate can quite obviously lead on to further cooperation in return.

What the competition had done was to recast Adam Smith's logic for the pacification process of trading into a game theoretic context. Trading should satisfy both parties, he'd said, so let the other fellow win as well, because this means you'll also be winning. In this way, Tit for Tat was showing that extending trust and friendship had to be the right way to proceed as it could lead to long-term, collaborative relationships.

When Axelrod came to write about his conclusions in *The Evolution of Cooperation*, he chose to describe Tit for Tat's robust achievements in human terms, and he used the simplest of descriptions to sum up how it worked:

First, he said, it was *nice*, in that the strategy meant one was never the person to initiate defection. In fact, if you were the player opening a new relationship - then you should always play Cooperate.

Then, secondly, it was *provokable* in that it could immediately retaliate if the other person played Defect… but that it also immediately *forgives* if he then reverted to choosing Cooperate. It didn't bear a grudge in other words, but just stuck to its tactic of always following what the opponent did.

Then came, perhaps, the most surprising of his insights. Axelrod summarises the approach by giving it the description of *don't be envious*. This is because Tit for Tat means that however many points you end up with, you can never score higher than the other person. At best, all you can hope for is that you're as good as him.

Wow. That seemed to be so weird and counterintuitive. How can you win by drawing or coming second?

It was, Axelrod said, because Tit for Tat succeeds by consistently racking up big scores… *by playing with a wide variety of partners.* Put another way, you shouldn't be concerned with winning individual contests, but instead should take the long view and concentrate on finding a number of separate cooperative partners. Then you could come out on top by picking up points from *all of them* over a lengthy period of time.

Next, Axelrod pointed out that the great strength of Tit for Tat was that it couldn't be more *open and clear*. Instead of having intricate strategies, or playing with a secret agenda, its whole approach was designed to tell your opponent exactly what you were doing, and exactly what they could expect from you. He called this final lesson: *don't be clever…* don't mess about, don't be enigmatic or inscrutable or tricky; don't be a smart arse.

'What accounts for Tit for Tat's robust success is its combination of being nice, retaliatory, forgiving and clear. Its niceness prevents it from getting into unnecessary trouble. Its retaliation discourages the other side from persisting whenever defection is tried. Its forgiveness helps restore mutual cooperation. And its clarity makes it intelligible to the other player, thereby eliciting long-term cooperation.'
Robert Axelrod, *The Evolution of Cooperation.*

So, what did it all add up to?

Perhaps most importantly, Axelrod's competition made plain that the Tit for Tat strategy showed up how the Hawk/Dove principle worked in action. Nasty, defector strategies might win against naïve, cooperative players, it said, but over time the retaliation mechanism of Tit for Tat was bound to come into its own. By doing this, it picks up maximum points when playing with cooperators, but when it meets a person who defects - it immediately switches to defection. And when Hawkish defectors are dealing with each other, then they're bound to attract fewer points between them.

Tit for Tat is therefore a strategy that *rewards cooperators and educates defectors*.

It succeeds over long periods of time in willing and repetitive relationships. It apes real life. The irony of its success is that a player who you would have said was being irrational in a one-time prisoner's dilemma by trusting his partner, is now seen as the person that's behaving rationally in the repeated game. He's now seen to be the calculating one, choosing partners to build high scoring relationships with - and punishing those who abuse his trust.

Axelrod said this long-term, repeated approach was central to the way that cooperation occurs naturally in life. Avoiding an end point, and so avoiding the game becoming finite instead of being iterated was key.

But what if that *did* happen? What if people were happily playing Always Cooperate, and then somebody suddenly decides to use the Defect choice because they want to scoop five points - and see that you get none?

Well, we all know how devastating that can be. Is there anything worse than being in a close relationship, and then being let down without any warning? In fact, the closer you'd been, the more shattering the betrayal. Or what about people who abuse a position of trust? Or those who are treacherous to their country? What horrible duplicity this is… no wonder we reserve our harshest punishments for traitors. All these sorts of things may leave a bad taste in the mouth, but they're all understandable in game theoretic logic.

So how did Axelrod's findings fit in with what had gone before? Well, perfectly. Tit for Tat may have shown itself to be another description for the biological mechanisms uncovered by Trivers and Maynard Smith, but it was also providing the solid, mathematical proofs for deeper truths about us humans and our social behaviour.

That was because although Tit for Tat might at first sight look as if it only explains how two people will play, it's actually also illustrating how the principle is then expanded into larger and more complex communities. What it highlights is how people will settle down to use Always Cooperate when they've shown each other that they're trustworthy. Cooperative individuals spread throughout society, and this then leads to its general morality. *In short, we're moral - and society becomes ethical - because we selfishly want the benefits that come from everyone being cooperative.*

But you're probably wondering why I suggested earlier that Axelrod's conclusions managed to please philosophers and religious leaders when the scholarly research logic of *The Evolution of Cooperation* first appeared. When people saw the implications, it wasn't long before many of them began to say: 'wait a minute... haven't we seen this before?'

In fact, isn't this exactly what we've always said?

This was because Tit for Tat was a game theoretic way of describing what religions term 'The Golden Rule'. It was, in essence, showing how genetic reciprocity could be given ethical clothes. Simply put, it's the way that we arrive at the moral obligation that one should treat others as one would like to be treated oneself. It was almost exactly the way Adam Smith had described the action of his Impartial Spectator. And what's more impartial than mathematical logic? The proof Axelrod had put together showed that the right way to play was to reciprocate with others... to see their needs through your eyes... and to see yourself through their eyes.

Whether we follow the instructions of monotheism, polytheism or humanism, every variant of these religious paths has at its heart the same message. Confucius, for example, was asked if there was one word that would summarise his message and he replied: 'Is not reciprocity such a word?' His contemporary, Lao Tse was similarly to say: 'Regard your neighbour's gain as your gain, and his loss as your loss.'

The Ancient Egyptians followed a similar code in that it spelt out: 'That which you hate to be done to you, do not do to another', and Socrates summed up the same message in the Greece of classical philosophy: 'Do not do unto others that which angers you when they do it to you.' The Hindus teach the same principle too: 'Treat others as you treat yourself.'

For some reason, many of the great religious figures of the Ancient World were plagued by smart alecs who'd hang around asking them trick questions. Jesus had quite a few of them. And his near contemporary, the rabbi and sage, Hillel, had one who asked him if he could recite the whole of the Torah while standing on one leg. Hillel famously stood like a stork while replying: 'That which is hateful to you, do not do to your fellow man. That is the whole Torah - the rest is explanation.'

As for Islam, there's a story about a man coming up to the Prophet when he was travelling on a camel and grabbing his foot as he begged to be told how to get to heaven. The Prophet replied: 'As you would have people do to you, do to them. And that which you dislike being done to you, don't do it to them... now, let go of the stirrup.'

Buddhists say: 'Hurt not others in ways that you yourself would find hurtful' and, as for Christianity, Tit for Tat's message is identical to the words of Jesus: '... so do unto others as you would have them do unto you.'

Each of these great religions has the same message of reciprocity. And yet each is game theoretic rather than divine. As Greg Epstein, the humanist chaplain at Harvard has pointed out: '... not a single one of these versions of the Golden Rule requires a God.'

But is this behaviour fundamentally selfish? Are we simply cooperating because we want cooperation in return? I suppose so, but does it matter... if we're doing good, isn't that enough? Does it undermine us if the Dilemma tells us we're doing it to get rewards? And although moral behaviour may have a selfish origin, haven't we learnt that altruism and virtue are attractive to other people, and that they lead to trusting relationships? Defectors may always look as if they're demanding reciprocity, but the truth is that cooperators want it as well... they're arguably just being more subtle in the way they're going about it.

We instinctively understand this great truth, even though we dislike admitting it to ourselves because we think it makes us look false. Perhaps it does. But we have to reconcile ourselves to the fact that all we're doing is behaving in the exact same way that every other creature in the natural world does, and has done since life began.

Our genes are making us want to win - and cooperation is a winning strategy. But this isn't genetic determinism because we still know that we can still ignore or override its orders if we want to. We have free will. We also have layers of convention that govern how we deal with others... but let's not pretend that we aren't capable of bluffing about how pure our motives might be.

Putting this in the form of a rather tough summation leads us to having to accept that: *we may wish to be collaborative, and appear as unselfish... but that's because we selfishly want the benefits that cooperation can bring.* Adam Smith was right - just leave us alone to interact and we'll produce order. But von Neumann was also right when he saw how this process works - that human existence is a colossal poker game.

What's plain is that the opposite is also true. Spongers, cheats, free riders, fakes and all the other people who defect and don't contribute, who fail to reciprocate when they're invited to collaborate, and who simply take rather than giving... all these and others like them have to be identified and excluded. If they're not, then they'll act like a virus by attaching themselves to productive lives, and then infecting a collaborative society by multiplying and spreading. No wonder our moral code seems to have been formed around the idea of punishing these threats. We all know we have to keep the number of defectors down if we're to keep their negative impact on society to a minimum.

The upshot of all this is that cooperators may have learnt not to be too demanding or precise about the need for exact exchanges or immediate returns... but that's not to say they don't expect to be paid back at some point in the future. However distant their horizons might be, or however patient even the most saintly of us can appear, our innate sense of fairness and social justice insists that we want our Tits to be eventually rewarded with Tats. After all, how many of us really don't care if we're endlessly taken for granted? Or exploited, or taken for a ride?

Visible acts of charity and compassion enhance our reputations, and we like being noticed for them. But as the point's been made before, we want some kind of return for our altruism, even if it's only an internalised sense of satisfaction, or perhaps something that ensures we get to heaven like a jet rocket.

Even so, there's a great paradox at work here because if we act with an entirely pure selflessness, then we lose control. If we 'abandon' ourselves to others, perhaps fall so deeply in love that we become completely slavish to another's needs rather than to our own, or act with manic altruism like poor George Price, then we're giving up our mechanism for weighing reciprocity. In short, we've stopped playing the game. This leads to us becoming dangerously exposed, and horribly vulnerable to exploitation.

> **'Love consists in giving without getting in return, in giving what is not owed,**
> **what is not due to the other. That's why true love is never based,**
> **as associations of utility or pleasure are, on a fair exchange.**
> **Mortimer Adler, *What Man Has Made of Man***

So, yes, we love the compassionate, the big-hearted, the charitable people in life and, yes, we hugely admire altruists and want as many of them in our societies as possible. And, yes too, the idea of us loving someone completely and profoundly is wonderful.

Then why aren't more of us like this? Why don't we always behave in the ways we so admire if it's clear how attractive this would make us? It's for the obvious reason that while it suits us to be the *object* of other people's giving, it costs us to be constantly handing it out ourselves. We like it, and praise it in others, but we don't want to run the risk of being taken advantage of by overdoing it ourselves.

> **'We are never so defenceless against suffering as when we love.'**
> **Sigmund Freud,** *A General Introduction to Psychoanalysis*

Now, don't imagine that I fail to understand how hard it is to accept the idea that cooperation has evolved in us. It goes against so many of the maxims and beliefs in life, doesn't it? We're so often told not to trust people, nor to be the first to offer something - and by doing this to avoid being taken for a sucker. More even than these, it's an accepted meme that if we were to scratch the surface gloss from most people, we'd find that they're selfish and grasping, just out for themselves. In fact, the evidence seems to be all around us. Humans may be clever, most of us think, but they're really a self-seeking bunch that'll go off the rails if they're given half a chance.

I also can't imagine there are many of us that don't know how bitter the taste of betrayal is. Being let down by people can undermine our faith in humanity. Add all these disappointments together and it's hardly surprising that we think mankind would descend into a state of anarchy and chaos if people didn't have the strong hand of authority to keep them in order. Cooperation sounds wonderful, but it also sounds utopian.

Whatever Robert Axelrod might say, surely these views have to be right? Can we ever truly reject the belief that personal greed would corrode our societies if it wasn't kept in check?

And so, in spite of what Mr Axelrod, Mr Smith, Mr Dawkins and all the others might say, don't we need to be constantly given laws, education, moral guidelines and punishments to keep us from tearing each other, and our poor world, apart?

Lifeboat ethics... not very ethical.

CHAPTER THIRTEEN

SO GAME THEORY'S CONCLUSION WAS THAT COOPERATION IS BOUND TO EVOLVE NATURALLY WITHIN SOCIETIES. BUT SURELY THAT HAS TO BE NONSENSE? DOESN'T EVERYONE AGREE THAT THE OPPOSITE IS TRUE. . . THAT UNLESS HUMANS ARE KEPT UNDER CONTROL, THEY'LL WRECK EVERYTHING WITH THEIR SELFISHNESS AND GREED?

On 14 September 2003, Professor Garrett Hardin and his wife, Jane, finally decided they'd had enough. He was 88 and she was 81, and although both had been in poor health for some time, they were clear in their own minds that there was still one final decision to be made.

The previous week they'd celebrated sixty-two years of marriage, but as their daughter, Sharon, was later to say: 'They were both members of the Hemlock Society and felt very strongly that they wanted to choose their own time to die.' Now, as they'd done throughout their lives, she said, their strong convictions meant they 'did what they wanted to do.'

And so, on that sad Sunday, one of the greatest gloom buckets of modern times decided to finish his life with the same kind of self-destructiveness that he'd spent so long arguing we humans were all bent on. He'd lectured for decades that mankind was irredeemably blind to its future, and that the more of us there were, the worse things would get. This meant, he said, that overpopulation was a ticking time bomb that would blow us all away.

At the very least, Hardin probably felt as he made his plans for their exits, if he and his wife were no longer exploiting the limited resources of what he called 'Spaceship Earth', then the two of them would be making one last contribution to its welfare.

But who was he? And why did he arrive at the conclusion that the very notion of humans working together, even cooperating, was a shallow-minded delusion? As far as he could see things, Tit for Tat would have just referred to one unspeakably selfish person grabbing yet more than another.

A zoologist by training, Hardin's outlook had been shaped from the outset by the many hardships he'd have experienced in his life. It was bad enough that he'd spent his childhood living in Dust Bowl poverty on his grandfather's Missouri farm, but he also had to contend with contracting polio, and the severe disabilities that the disease had left him with.

Bullied at school for his shortened leg, it's just possible that iron entered his soul as he tried to avoid his blockhead, barnyard tormentors. Was it even possible that in some secret way he felt these ruffian types had *less* of a right to life than clever people like himself? No amount of fame or distinguished scholarship would ever seem to completely melt the suspicion.

Human existence, he *knew*, was a dog-eat-dog affair in which our self-centred compulsions would have dire consequences for the whole race. The only way to save us, he maintained, was with a combination of statistical proof, the imposition of hard-headed moral guidelines, tough laws and government actions. If we managed this then it was just possible we might accept that however horrible the means might be, the end results would be completely justified.

'We're doomed!'

For Hardin this wasn't some kind of airy-fairy discussion about the social contract. He wasn't interested in arguments about the role of cooperation as a life force - that might sometimes be the case in normal times - but when resources become scarce, he said, then man's true nature was exposed. And what was that true nature? Ah, he was quite certain about that. It was, he argued, pure selfishness.

You'd have thought that Hardin's doctoral specialism in microbial symbioses might have opened up his thinking to the potential for mutual gains. Yet by the time he came to take up the post of Professor of Human Ecology at the University of California, he knew that his life's work was to warn the rest of us that it was hopeless to ever expect selfless or synergistic collaborations to solve the world's problems.

From the time he first joined the research institute at Santa Barbara in 1946, he set about assembling the data to support his dystopian views. At base he was a confirmed neo-Malthusian, convinced that no 'technical' advances in providing food security would ever meet the demands of an exploding global population. The world's resources, he never grew tired of saying, were finite, and this meant they could only ever support a finite population.

Yes, there might be uplifts from higher agricultural yields, or things like new strains of wheat, but these would simply never improve the 'carrying capacity' of the Earth's landmass to the point where it could provide the energy needs of future generations. If people continued to overbreed in the manner they were, he said, then the only way of looking at our behaviour was as some kind of collective suicide pact. Like Malthus had before him, he saw nothing but bleakness and destruction for the human race.

But why, you're no doubt thinking, did he believe we were all so awful and stupid that we'd march blindly off the cliff edge of survival? Why did he think that the devastation of our species was such a racing certainty - and why couldn't we adjust our behaviour to fix things in the ways we'd managed with everything else?

The answer was the reverse of what Robert Axelrod would later find in his competition. Hardin's vision was the polar opposite to the findings that would come in *The Evolution of Cooperation*. Instead of our life forces leading to growing levels of collaboration, Hardin was convinced that the opposite was true… and that human interactions would inevitably become stuck in a one-way ratchet of *Always Defect*.

His logic went like this. If the Earth's energy resources weren't subject to government control, then no society would ever be able to share things out fairly. Greed, suspicion and selfishness would run riot because each person would always defend themselves against other people who were taking too much.

Take a piece of common land as an example, he said. The commoners might have grazed it for generations with everyone putting out a few head of cattle. But the system was always on the verge of abuse. Say an individual was to put out more cows than people thought was his right... then what would his neighbour do? Well, he'd be a fool to let the man get away with it.

He, too, would increase his herd. Soon everybody else would respond in the same way. They'd have to wouldn't they? If they didn't, they'd be fools for letting other people walk all over them. The selfish behaviour of their neighbours would have made them lose out.

So what happened under these circumstances? Everyone might have just been defending their corner, but soon there would be more cattle on the commons than the land could support. It was bound to become overgrazed and collapse. It would never be given the time to recover. And so the food supply would dry up... and the community starve.

Hardin formalised this doom-laden scenario into a hugely influential paper in 1968 called *The Tragedy of the Commons*. It became the cornerstone of a new kind of data-driven view of our social future. According to him the outlook might be bleak, but it was logical, and it could only be avoided in one of two ways - or possibly by a combination of them. Either, he said, governments should take over the world's energy resources, particularly land management, and impose laws that would limit our natural, self-centred rapacity.

Or if not that, then the resources should be split apart, parcelled up and privatised. Owners would then be motivated to run and preserve them better than any bunch of quarrelling individuals ever could. And people certainly would squabble if this didn't happen - of that he was quite certain - because they'd never agree on dividing things up fairly when they had so little to base their actions on, other than some vague hope of finding goodwill between the parties.

As Hardin's gloomy conclusions became more widely read and the idea of a global 'Commons' took root in the public's consciousness, so his blanket lack of faith in humans and public policies became increasingly exposed. Why, he began asking, if food and other resources were going to run out... why didn't the burgeoning overpopulation reduce itself in a natural, Darwinian response?

He now began to take the gloves off: why didn't the awful, low grade types that were obviously unable to limit their grotesque breeding habits simply die off? If they were so wildly overbreeding, then their inferior offspring should logically be less able to take care of themselves. They should therefore naturally decline. 'Parents who breed too exuberantly', he wrote, 'would leave fewer dependents, not more, because they were unable to care adequately for their children.' In fact, wasn't this exactly why the 'backward races' always had so many children?

Phew. Strong stuff, even then. But completely jaw-dropping from the historical perspective we have now. Looking back at this period, it seems strange that demonstrations were taking place against EO Wilson's views on human nature, and yet just a few years earlier, Hardin was able to put forward these kinds of arguments with such an astonishing lack of restraint.

But that was the spirit of the age. Birth rates and immigration levels were, indeed, increasing fast, and many people thought that end-of-the-world scenarios weren't far behind.

In the same year that *The Tragedy of the Commons* appeared, for example, a highly respected Stanford Professor of Population Studies called Paul Ehrlich published *The Population Bomb*, a nightmarish warning that hundreds of millions of people were going to starve to death because of unchecked overpopulation. (Ehrlich was later to be proved so irresponsible, and so utterly wrong, that even he had to end up acknowledging how absurd he'd been. Nonetheless, at the time there was a huge audience for what he was saying, only too prepared to believe that his despair-ridden forecasts were accurate.)

If Hardin's logic was right, then the cheats and free riders being shown up as anti-social defectors in the prisoner's dilemma, together with what he saw as a moronic, grasping underclass… should all decline in a vast, global Darwinian die-off. But this wasn't happening. Why not, he demanded to know, before going on to answer his own question.

**'Darwinism by itself did not produce the Holocaust, but without Darwinism…
neither Hitler nor his Nazi followers would have had the necessary
scientific underpinnings to convince themselves and their collaborators that one
of the world's greatest atrocities was really morally praiseworthy.'
Richard Weikart, *From Darwin to Hitler: Evolutionary Ethics,
Eugenics and Racism in Germany***

It was being averted, he said, because of the squeamishness of modern liberal opinion.

The problem was that the richer countries had welfare systems, and these were getting in the way of natural selection… and keeping what he saw as lesser breeds alive. This intervention was upsetting the natural order. Worse, the world's sentimental conscience was leading to misplaced sympathy for the backward populations of other countries. In short, he said, aid and welfare programmes were accentuating the problem. Donations were helping the wrong people to survive.

I know, it's hardly believable is it? And yet he then went further, and concluded that charitable giving and technical assistance were counter-productive. Why, he demanded to know, did liberals always say: 'There is a shortage of food. Why don't we say, there is a longage of people?'

Then in 1974, he took the *Tragedy* on to a new level in a famous article entitled *Lifeboat Ethics: The Case Against Helping The Poor*. If the numbers were so relentless in their message, he was now saying, humans had to stomach some harsh medicine or the patient wouldn't survive the disease. In the article, he asked its readers to imagine that the productive and prosperous people of a country were in a lifeboat, floating on the surface of an ocean. Around them in the water were poor immigrants and other 'inferior types'. If all these people tried to scramble into the lifeboat, he said, it would capsize and everyone would drown.

His horrible argument continued: if anyone was going to survive the impending calamity, then surely it should be the more advanced classes? If intelligence was hereditary, and poor people kept overbreeding… then inevitably the average IQ of the world would decline. The only thing that would increase was human misery.

The proof for this assertion? The richer, developed nations were doubling their populations every 87 years, while the countries who produced the sorts of people who were swimming in the ocean were only taking 35. The poor, his conclusion shrieked, were the ones overgrazing the 'Commons'.

So what was his medicine? Well, if individuals wouldn't do it for themselves, then their governments had to. Programmes should be introduced to control birth rates with planned populations, contraception, abortions, sterilisation, coercion and 'lifeboat ethics'. If we were capable of passing legislation against robbery and violence, then why couldn't we do the same thing against people who were putting the entire species in danger?

> 'In a competitive world of limited resources, total
> freedom of individual action is intolerable.'
> Garrett Hardin, *The Tragedy of the Commons*

The globe's landmasses and seas, Hardin continued, were the ultimate 'Commons' because they were a shared resource. And yet human selfishness, defector types, developing nations and the population explosion were all leading to a Malthusian catastrophe. How would people behave under these circumstances? Badly. 'Freedom to breed', he shrieked, 'is intolerable'.

If this logic meant the better-off had to stop the poor from getting in the lifeboat, or throw them overboard, then so be it. 'Injustice', Hardin thundered, 'is preferable to total ruin... those who are biologically more fit to be the custodians of property and power should legally inherit more.'

Even by the social attitudes of the time, Hardin looked as if he'd gone too far. More to the point, he couldn't have been more wrong.

As the years went by, the evidence against him piled up. Since the *Tragedy of the Commons* was first published in 1968, not a single country in the world has increased its birth rate. By the time of his death, thirty five years later, the global population had doubled, yet average incomes had trebled. Food security had wildly improved, yields had multiplied, incidents of famine and starvation had fallen sharply, mortality rates plummeted, particularly among children, education levels boomed, the number of democracies mushroomed, global income inequalities narrowed, and world poverty had embarked on a steep decline.

And yet Garrett Hardin never relented. Logic remained on his side, he insisted. Humans could never be trusted to govern themselves. Adam Smith was entirely wrong, the Invisible Hand was a hoax, faith in free markets was for the feeble-minded, and the use of game theory to show how cooperation emerged was nonsense and... well, you'll see.

Of course, as time passed, he was increasingly seen as bonkers: a eugenicist, a racist, white supremacist, head-in-the-sand ignorer of the data, and all-round grumpy git. He didn't stop at just the 'Commons'. 'Mindless music' in public places, jet engine noise, radio programmes interrupted by advertising, the visual damage of billboards. All terrible. All examples of the way individual selfishness damages society.

And yet... here was a highly intelligent man who was arguing with stubborn courage that the mathematical logic of the prisoner's dilemma had to be flashing continuous warning signs. Why wouldn't people snatch at five points if the opportunity arose, and they thought they could get away with it?

Perhaps he was right? Cooperation is always available - and yet everyone cheats if they're given a sniff of not being spotted. So why wouldn't desperate people cheat more than the better off? And if there are too many of them... then society will surely break down?

He wasn't alone in these views. Others had said much the same thing in previous generations. Alfred Russel Wallace had come out with some ghastly stuff, and Darwin's own son, Leonard, was a ferociously outspoken eugenicist.

> **'It is indisputably the mediocre, if not the low, both as regards morality and intelligence, who are successful in life and multiply the fastest.'**
> **Alfred Russel Wallace, *Darwinism***

However, around the time Hardin was sounding off, there was a major appetite for this kind of rabid pessimism. Over the course of his life he alone published over 350 articles and twenty-seven books with total sales of some 700,000 copies. He was convinced of his logic, and many people agreed.

It was almost as if scientists like him were going through a kind of thrashing death dance before the modern understanding of the role of the gene opened biologists' eyes to more enlightened theories.

What Hardin had to say sounds absurd to our modern sensibilities, yet he spoke in a warm-hearted, kindly way. He assembled his facts meticulously, and recognised that his message sounded harsh. Nonetheless, he saw himself as doing the vital work of saving the world from itself. Messengers were often put to death when they were the bearers of bad news, he'd have said, but people still needed to receive the message.

And was he entirely wrong?

Game theory shows us that the world's defectors are always trying to get an advantage over their fellow man. We do behave selfishly. We do rip fossil fuels out of the ground without much thought for their replacement. We do pollute ceaselessly, spoiling our planet for future generations. And we do overfish the oceans, depleting them in exactly the way that Hardin spoke about his mythical 'Commons'.

Maybe the logic of the iterated prisoner's dilemma was wrong? Was it possible that the conclusion that cooperation would naturally evolve only worked in theory… and that humans actually behaved like rats in a sack if they came under the pressure of supplies running short?

Was it possible, in fact, that the endless tension between zero sum and non-zero forces, the individual and society, and all the other discussions about the best way to survive in life, all arrived at the conclusion that humans had somehow moved away from having an evolutionary stable strategy? Perhaps we were simply incapable of ever sharing things up fairly?

Well, it's at this stage that a truly heroic figure enters the story… someone who was going to use the same weapons of case histories and research data to present a completely different version of how we strange, human creatures manage to get along with each other.

Who was that?

Her name was Elinor Ostrom.

Lin Ostrom receiving the Nobel Prize from
King Carl Gustaf of Sweden. Would an Oscar
have been better?

CHAPTER FOURTEEN

ELINOR OSTROM? WHO WAS SHE? ANOTHER PERSON WHO BELIEVED HUMANS WERE DOOMED BY THEIR SELFISHNESS? OR DID SHE THINK THAT COOPERATION MIGHT POSSIBLY EMERGE AS WE DEALT WITH EACH OTHER?

Lin Ostrom wasn't someone blessed with the most helpful of backgrounds for winning the Nobel Prize... particularly for such a rigorously forensic and evidence-based subject as Economics. Where she came from was the very opposite of these things: a world of make-believe and vapid images, the smoke and ornate mirrors of the golden years of Hollywood.

Born Elinor Awan in 1933, she was the only child of a set designer and a musician, the kind of people who somehow survived on the rackety fringes of the movie business. They'd separated when she was very young, and Lin was then shuttled between the two of them experiencing, like Garrett Hardin himself, the poverty of the post-Depression years.

Again like Hardin, she'd had to overcome prejudice and bullying when she was at Beverly Hills High School, and this was followed by real hardship as she tried to scrape together enough money to establish herself as a scientist.

By the late 1950s she was just another female struggling to make her way in a man's world. She found work as an export clerk, a secretary, and then eventually as an assistant personnel manager for a firm that had never hired a woman into a managerial position before. An early marriage broke up, but she slogged on alone, saving dollar by measly dollar to put the funds together to pay her way through a post-graduate programme.

She was nearly thirty when she was finally accepted by UCLA for the PhD that was to define her life. Qualified at last, she married a social scientist named Vincent Ostrom, a man nearer to Garrett Hardin's age than her own, and together they were to devote their lives to proving that the counsel of despair behind his pessimism, and the logic of the *Tragedy of the Commons*, was profoundly wrong-headed.

Communities, Lin would dedicate herself to showing, were perfectly capable of avoiding the Malthusian catastrophes of starvation, selfishness and warfare that so many believed defined our futures.

Instead, she set out to show that the opposite was true: that Tragedies didn't have to happen, and that although the process might be lengthy and reliant on compromise, individuals would ultimately show themselves as willing to collaborate. They would, she insisted, take effective action to avoid disasters. In particular, their instinct was to work together, ensuring that what she termed 'common pool resources' (CPRs) could be preserved, maintained and even fairly shared out.

Just as Adam Smith had seen before her, Lin Ostrom was certain that if people had good information about the dangers that could affect them, then they'd act in their collective self-interests.

She believed that far from this having selfish consequences, the motivation of individuals who were looking out for themselves would lead to a process that increased the common good.

People weren't stupid was her guiding principle. They weren't deaf to arguments, nor blind to 'the shadow of the future'. And they certainly weren't immune to the gains that arose from cooperation. However stubborn or hard-headed their inhabitants might be, communities would be only too aware that a *Tragedy of the Commons* awaited them if they didn't sort things out for themselves.

Because of this, she said, people sharing problems like a limited resource didn't have to depend on top-down regulations to tell them what to do. In fact, government interventions could be bureaucratically heavy-handed, and insensitive to local needs, and this often made them counterproductive to good outcomes. Instead, what people needed to reach equitable agreements were communication, information, space and time… but if they had these, then without doubt, *collaboration would evolve between the parties.*

'It didn't take (Ostrom) long to realise there was one crucial detail Hardin's paper had overlooked. Humans can talk. Farmers and fishermen and neighbours are perfectly capable of making agreements to keep their fields from turning into deserts, their lakes from being overfished and their wells from drying out.'
Rutger Bregman, *Humankind*

Nonetheless, Lin Ostrom realised that the sorts of game theoretic arguments that other researchers were using would never be enough to convince the sceptics. Cooperation might get going in lab experiments like Axelrod's... but most people would never be dissuaded from the view that when real life had to be faced, and questions of life and death took hold, people would trample all over each other.

If she was really going to show how conflicting interests could fairly share out CPRs (rather than have regulatory bodies do it for them) then she'd need the hard evidence of successful case histories.

For her doctorate she'd intensively studied the local history about how the California water wars had eventually been resolved, even though the competing sides had always appeared to be in completely intractable opposition. There could hardly be a more cast iron example of how people playing Always Defect would end up in a stalemate. And yet somehow, even the greed and obstinacy of the two sides in this long-running conflict had somehow managed to come to an accommodation. But how was that?

Winning the water wars had involved years of fighting between the toughest of hombres on the make, men half crazed with frontier ambition. Their struggles had begun as far back as the late 19th century when it had become plain that the future of the embryonic city of Los Angeles was going to depend on getting fresh water from the snowmelt of the Sierra Nevada mountain range. But that was nearly four hundred miles away to the north, and the Owens River run-off that carried it away had to pass through the vastness of the Owens Valley, the deepest depression in the US, before the water could make its way down towards the growing city.

Make that happen, the builders, local politicians, investors and engineers all knew, and they'd build a great commercial capital for the West Coast. Failing to do so, the water superintendent, William Mulholland was to famously tell them, would be self-defining: 'If you don't get the water, you won't need it!'

The battles raged for over fifty years. Speculators and insiders cheated, lied and used every other kind of underhand trick to buy up key plots of land. By 1905 they'd reputedly embezzled their way to owning 95% of the valley floor. In an ironic reverse of the *Tragedy of the Commons*, the remaining ranchers and farmers now came under acute financial pressure to keep going, because so few of them were left to share the costs of maintaining the infrastructure.

In 1913 the ruthless Mulholland diverted the Owens river and then built a gravity-fed, 233-mile aqueduct that channelled water south to the thirsty citizens of LA. In 1923 the remaining farmers formed a cooperative and the following year they rebelled, with parts of the aqueduct being destroyed by dynamite.

Agricultural interests were now in open conflict with the residential needs of the booming city. Both were desperate for fresh water. Neither would relent. The rampant greed of the two sides continued, and chicanery, subterfuge, bribery, spying and secret deals were common. It was a time of thugs and strong-arm tactics, threats, false draughts and double-crosses.

Eventually the aqueduct was rebuilt, and in 1941 an extension was added to meet the needs of the expanding suburbs. Anyone who's seen Roman Polanski's masterpiece, *Chinatown*, will know how dirty the fight was - but the film's plot lines were only the final chapters of a long running war in which fortunes were being made by increasingly 'respectable' businessmen.

The movie sums up just how corrosive power can become when John Huston's character, the worldly yet brutal tycoon, Noah Cross ('Of course I'm respectable. I'm old. Politicians, public buildings, and whores all get respectable if they last long enough') is exposed as stopping at nothing to buy land that will wildly increase in value if he secures the water rights.

As he says in one of the film's great lines: 'Most people never have to face the fact that at the right time and the right place, they're capable of *anything*.' Horrible.

And yet, and yet. However opposed even the most intransigent ranchers and Hawkish monsters like Noah Cross might have been, Lin Ostrom was able to demonstrate that a shared vision of the future hung over even the most self-serving of negotiations and tactics. The wars eventually ended in cooperation. As the hard edges of their strategies were rubbed down over time, the parties eventually worked things out for themselves, compromising if they had to, even accepting that they might have to be the junior partner in the symbiotic settlements.

Everybody knew that there was only one source of the water, only one Sierra Nevada. The common pool resource simply had to be shared. And once the old enemies had finally sorted themselves out, they'd then been content to hand over their private agreements and contracts to be signed into law.

The bottom-up process was the ultimate winner... in just the way that Robert Axelrod was to show in his computer programmes. Once hostility had given way to informed negotiations, farmers came to realise that the soil qualities of the Owens and San Fernando valleys meant they were never going to be the agricultural paradises they'd hoped for.

Indeed, those that had resisted the early pressure to sell actually ended up getting substantially more leasing income than if they'd retained the land for ranching. The 'water wars' turned into peace... and became one of the most carefully researched examples of how utility markets could work effectively.

Lin and Vincent - by now recognised for his own work on the same subject with his paper *The Organisation of Government in Metropolitan Areas* - moved on to Indiana University. Here they opened a workshop in Political Theory and Policy Analysis, set up and designed expressly to research other examples of bottom-up cooperation.

These case histories would be needed to back up Lin's conviction that if people were sufficiently incentivised and informed, then they wouldn't need the 'command and control' process of being told what to do by a Big Man or a government. Once collaboration was initiated, she said, the parties' agreements could later be formalised through legislation and regulation.

One of the masterful negotiators of Maine.

Together with her colleagues and students at Indiana, she was to spend the rest of her life disproving the assumption that commonly held resources were free-for-alls. As the *Financial Times* was to summarise her refutation of Hardin's ideas: 'The Commons were owned by a community. They were managed by a community. These people were neighbours. In many cases, they set their own rules. Lin Ostrom knew there was nothing inevitable about the self-destruction of CPRs... the *Tragedy of the Commons* wasn't a tragedy at all. It was a problem - and problems have solutions.'

Between 1974 and her death in 2012, Lin Ostrom's team examined over a thousand separate examples in which common pool resources were managed at a local level. In each case they were controlled by internal rules that the participants had themselves evolved. From places and people as diverse as the Swiss cattle herders in their Alpine pastures, through the lobster catchers of the Maine coast, to Turkish fishing communities, water management in Nepal and forest conservation in Sri Lanka, each was closely examined and catalogued.

The workshop studied satellite data, interviewed individuals in their villages and fishing ports, and spoke to countless government officials, aid organisations and local researchers. Once they'd interrogated the results, they then used game theoretic techniques to mathematically cast the participants' differing interests.

The team peered deeply into the range of methods people used to maintain resources from oil fields to aquifers. And everywhere they looked, they found examples of human ingenuity producing fair outcomes.

Just as trading techniques and specialisation and exchange had become so successful in our cultural evolution without a top-down hand directing them, so Lin Ostrom managed to show that people were as capable of avoiding tragedies as they were of creating gains.

Sometimes her team found participants reaching their agreements through discussion, sometimes they'd be employing lotteries or the drawing of lots, sometimes even - as in the original commons of mediaeval times - people would 'stint' themselves by reducing rather than increasing their shareholdings. In other cases there'd be strict rotations, and sometimes even the imposition of penalties in the form of internally set fines and exclusions.

But always, she and her students found there'd been the evolution of mutually agreed solutions, of accommodations that met the other party halfway, and crucially a recognition of the rights of others. These might take time to bubble up and then be formalised between them, but they would usually involve variants of the same kinds of policing systems, sanctions, negotiating procedures, monitoring and conflict resolution mechanisms.

The Indiana workshop found that solutions might involve lengthy and long-winded local arguments, even errors along the way, but there was always an underlying recognition that individual greed shouldn't be allowed to end in collective disaster.

In the end, Lin Ostrom's conclusion was that there was no single panacea for how CPRs should be managed, a finding that offended academics who were always looking to arrive at neat solutions. Instead, her team recorded any number of wonderfully inventive fixes that led to her coming up with the famous, worldly maxim of Ostrom's Law: 'A resource arrangement that works in practice can work in theory.'

What this meant, she said, was that solutions would emerge through the gradual evolution of 'subsystem variables': factors such as how many people were using a resource, what its size was, its predictability, importance, collective usage, historical rules and so on.

The critical finding was that there was never such a thing as a 'one size fits all'. Just like Adam Smith's Man of System who 'couldn't suffer the slightest deviation' to his plans, top-down solutions were almost bound to fail. This was because none of them ever seemed to recognise the unique demands of local issues, nuances that only bottom-up processes would ever manage to work their way around.

As Lin Ostrom was to say: 'There is no reason to believe that bureaucrats and politicians, no matter how well meaning they are, are better at solving problems than the people on the spot, who have the strongest incentive to get the solution right.' In putting it in these terms she completely rejected the idea of people as dumb participants, pathetic shoulder-shruggers who'd be looking on helplessly while their resources were destroyed.

Together, Lin and Vincent developed the concept of 'polycentric' strategies, in which solutions to complex problems didn't always have to be based on a single mechanism. Those that seemed to work best were invariably the ones taken closest to the resource. In general, the more remote the decision-makers were, the worse the outcomes.

In 1990 she published her collective findings in a landmark book that specifically repudiated Hardin's message called *Governing the Commons: The Evolution of*

Institutions for Collective Action. In this, she concluded from the evidence that the actors most affected by loss from a depleted resource were the ones best placed to create appropriate institutions. In summary, her arguments ran against either statist or market solutions.

Lin Ostrom won the Nobel Prize in 2009 to the astonishment of many of her ostensibly more eminent colleagues. Modest as ever, she donated the $1.5m prize to her 'family' at the workshop, and then quietly carried on with what so many people regarded as her profoundly important project. Her co-winner that year was Professor Oliver Williamson of Berkeley who called her 'a great human being' with a wonderful sense of joy, and a passion for nurturing young people. She died three years later - while reviewing a student's thesis in her hospital bed. Vincent followed a few days later.

So who was right in their views on human self-interest? Was it the old misery guts, Garrett Hardin, so certain in his pessimism about mankind's inability to avoid tragedies? Or was it Lin Ostrom with her 'sparkling laugh' and deep faith in humanity's ability to project forward, and see how problems would develop in the future if we didn't fix things?

Unlike her, Hardin was convinced that we were so irredeemably selfish that we'd rather wreck a shared asset instead of trying to preserve it through cooperation and fairness. He was to spend years ranting at the stupidity of others, convinced that they were blindly increasing the population - yet he and his wife brought four children into the world, well beyond the general birth rate of the time.

In his vision we were all so dogged by our greedy natures that we could only be tamed by the harsh imposition of a governmental approach. The only future for humans, he was sure, was for us to be supervised by a version of Hobbes's *Leviathan*, an external body that knew better than us little people about how to arrive at the greater good.

Yet Lin Ostrom was a woman whose whole life was dedicated to showing that we could make the world a better place, whatever the size of our population. Unlike Hardin, she was never to add to the world's total, ending her life childless, even though her students called her Grandma. Like Adam Smith's vision of the Impartial Spectator, her belief was that one had to see things from the other man's point of view. If people did this then they'd arrive at joint decisions about how best to tackle issues such as sharing a precious resource.

Again, like Smith before her, she believed that individual self-interest would inevitably lead to the best outcomes for the whole community. If people were left alone to work things out for themselves, both of them would argue, they'd produce order, not create chaos.

What each of them had concluded was that we don't need remote institutions telling us what to do; we don't want to be controlled by outside experts, or threatened by Big Men. Governments work best, so many of us feel, when the heat of human creativity is contained within one of Adam Smith's 'fire baskets'. When solutions are generated from the bottom upwards, legislation and regulations should follow.

The bureaucrat's instinct is to know better than the little guys, but both Smith and Ostrom were convinced that officials had to put their pride in their pockets, and instead believe in people's collective genius for arriving at win-win solutions. This was the non-zero process of trading - of thinking through to how solving the other man's problems would also solve your own.

As they did this, neighbours would be using commercial logic and negotiation to arrive at profitable outcomes. Once they'd achieved that, then our unique human ability to alter our behaviour would lead people to be flexible when it came to resolving social problems.

> **'Cooperation is maintained by the interaction of**
> **reciprocity, reputation and trust - and not by altruism.'**
> **David Sloane Wilson, *The Tragedy of the Commons:***
> ***How Elinor Ostrom Solved One of Life's Greatest Dilemmas***

We also love the idea of having faith in our fellow man, because we feel compassion for others on a personal level. Most of us would instinctively prefer to win without seeing someone else lose. And we also want the personal warmth and generosity of people like Lin Ostrom to be regarded as better than Hardin's negativity... a negativity that seems to arise so often in the minds of very clever people when they apply their reasoning to proving that because A is leading to B, then it will inevitably lead to C. Yes, it may do, but the same logic doesn't necessarily mean that it then has to lead to D.

Whether mankind is essentially 'good' or 'bad' is one of those arguments that have knocked around since the *H. sapiens* species first picked up the language trick. Hardin and Ostrom simply found a context to throw the debate into the sharpest of focuses. Yet if one steps back to take in the entire sweep of evolution, it's increasingly clear that the terms are meaningless. As organisms search for their individual survival strategies, everything in life employs both zero sum and non-zero tactics - and we humans are no different.

We all have Hawkish and Dovish aspects to our behavioural strategies. Since this is the case, then why should these strategies be viewed as understandable survival tactics in lower life forms - and yet be clouded in a moral light when we see them in ourselves? We might scoff at 'the law of the jungle' yet Nature's survival strategies are not laws but systems - and systems that are so breathtakingly intricate that they've allowed organisms to survive for millions of years longer longer than we humans have.

Lin Ostrom's work can now be seen to be sending us an even more powerful message than simply quashing the belief that we are all selfish egoists, bent only on our own survival. It's not just CPR's that we're able to preserve, but the fact that we're perfectly capable of making up our own minds about how we wish to behave with others, and what kind of lives we want to have. Yet this simple insight infuriates those people who 'know better' than we do.

The shortcomings of government officials were highlighted in Ostrom's work… but what about the smug attitudes of individuals, lobbying groups and social commentators who are also convinced that their fellow man is stupid or vile - and that they themsleves are not? Why do they always insist on telling others what to do and think, and become so outraged on other people's behalf - even though these same people might not be? And why are these types so certain they're right that they're quick to call anyone who disagrees with them uncaring and heartless?

These 'I care more than you do' activists are instinctively authoritarian, convinced they're right, immune to the Impartial Spectator's judgement, and unable to imagine that ordinary citizens can be trusted to come to their own conclusions.

Most of them have the same conviction that they're always in the right that the puffed-up Big Men of our past did. Unlike them they may not want physical control over people's lives - but they certainly want thought control. But just like them, they're forever demanding tough rules for what they see as the unfeeling morons that surround them, convinced that only they know the answers in life. And that the masses know nothing.

They are, in short, nothing but Hawks - in spite of thinking that they're the opposite. They all, of course, sneer at politicians, but they're just as guilty of patronising attitudes as any elected official - frequently more so when they display their self-righteous outlooks and absurd virtue signalling. No wonder they're destined to fall out with each other in the same way as Hawks do: they think only *they* are right; they have no patience or instinctive kindness for others, and no belief in man's natural wish to collaborate.

Much as we might want to cooperate to deal with our problems, however, our world is currently faced with colossal global resource challenges. Pollution is rampant, whole countries seem to think they can export their damage onto others, synthetic materials like plastics are mindlessly thrown away, growing carbon levels are due largely to selfish behaviour, entire nations clearly take more than their share of what's available, and changes to the world's climate require urgent, coordinated actions.

Can we really wait for 'local' solutions to arise when these kinds of issues straddle borders? We live in a connected, globalised world in which everyone is affected by the destruction of our oceans, lakes, forests, waterways and atmosphere. The air we breathe and the water we drink are no longer contained in just a neighbourhood. The common pool resource that's now under threat is a worldwide issue.

Nonetheless, there are signs that the problems are being tackled - and certainly being treated as a high priority. The levels of general concern and information now mean that the scale of the crisis is no longer being swept under the carpet. It's apparent that unless the causes can be fixed, the potential outcomes are very damaging indeed. The participants in this global 'Commons' are now open to the arguments and motivated to achieve change, largely because sentiment has decisively swung away from narrow, regional interests and towards a recognition of the need for global reforms.

The evidence of this seems pretty widespread now. There's a universal 'mood' to solve them and I deal with many of the initiatives being enacted in the last book of this series. The sight of Greta Thunberg, a scowling schoolgirl, being given free rein to scold the serried ranks of UN delegates that they'd 'stolen her childhood', shows just little counter argument there is. She and others like her may not be offering practical solutions, but they're very obviously having a marked effect on getting governments to work on real, 'polycentric' solutions, rather than just putting out honeyed statements of intent.

When the French political analyst, Alexis de Tocqueville, crossed the Atlantic to look at American prison conditions in the early 19th century, he stayed for a number of months to observe how the process of US democracy worked.

Initially he'd scoffed at the absence of radical actions from Big Men there, using the command and control, centrally developed edicts he saw in Europe. But the longer he studied how the deal-making of self-interested parties could arrive at equitable outcomes, the more he came to admire the vigour that made true bottom-up processes accomplish things. In fact, he concluded that they led to far longer-lasting solutions than any dictatorial system ever could, however benign their powers might be.

> 'Far from being truly altruistic, the cooperative person is merely looking to his long-term self-interest, rather than the short-term'.
> Matt Ridley, *The Origins of Virtue*

Lin Ostrom could see exactly the same forces at work that de Tocqueville had. He had come to regard American democracy as having evolved to be as near as possible to a perfected form - but he could also see that it was a confused and messy business in the way it arrived at decisions and compromises. Yet many commentators continue to conclude that when a society listens to the wishes of its affected people, then the most fair and enduring solutions emerge. Forced plants, history seems to show us, rarely do as well as those that are allowed the time and space to put down a deep root system.

But if all this is true... then why has mankind behaved with such unreal levels of destruction in the past? In fact, why has this kind of negative behaviour almost defined our history?

The only credible explanation for it is that, until very recently, human communities were dominated by Big Men and their grabbing sidekicks. And they all followed the same playbook of acting in their own selfish interests and telling the rest of us what to do. In terms of our cultural evolution, we only really began to acquire the information we needed to think for ourselves in recent history.

Widespread knowledge only arrived with the mass printing of books and pamphlets and the expansion of literacy. Ever since then, of course, we've witnessed the incredible growth of data that's been made available from books, newspapers, TV and other media platforms. However, all this has only arrived in the past couple of hundred years. Before that pretty well everyone was in the dark and manipulated by myths and endless anxiety.

The internet and social media have now added a further influence to the global demand for solutions. The result of this is that billions of us are now actively involved in understanding the problems of our global CPRs and other social problems. Governments have no place to hide any longer - particularly if they wish to be re-elected - and even their usual attempts at putting out misleading information, or simply procrastinating, are rebounding on them. Since the problems are now inarguable… we have to believe that solutions will follow.

All these forces can now be cast in the language of game theory. Tit for Tat cuts through the obfuscations of deniers and patronage. People are now showing their hunger for cooperation - and they're not going to put up with 'defecting' rulers. Most of us recognise that the mess we've made has been the price of economic progress, but we want it cleaned up. Axelrod's findings would suggest that overall levels of collaboration are bound to increase and, personally, I have complete faith that Lin Ostrom's predictions will be proven correct. People will collectively solve their CPR problems in the future, just as they've always done so in the past.

'Many problems that challenge us today can be traced back to a profound tension between what's good and desirable for society as a whole and what is good and desirable for an individual… global problems such as climate change, pollution, resource depletion… overpopulation. Now, more than ever, the world needs SuperCooperators.'
Martin Nowak, *SuperCooperators*

All good… yet the elephant in the room still stands there trumpeting. That's because we're still surrounded by evidence of the opposite of cooperation. Unyielding enmities are everywhere: politicians have a visceral loathing for each other, couples are locked in mutually intransigent marriages, uncompromising hatreds abound, inflexible attitudes keep whole peoples apart, and unremitting vendettas are the stuff of folk legend.

Yes, Anatol Rapoport may have exposed how Tit for Tat achieved the most points, but the strategy also shows how playing Defect will logically be met with the response of Defect in reply. Incipient feuds are therefore endlessly possible. The threat of Always Defect hangs over every exchange, because the different sides can be dragged into a pit of low scoring if neither of them reaches out to the other.

In other words, obdurate hostilities will intensify and everything can get bogged down by a continuous lack of trust. It might still be a Tit for Tat… but what an awful outcome. How can it ever be reversed?

In short, how did game theory suggest that *cooperation could ever be restored in these circumstances?*

Gustave Dore's illustration of *Belling the Cat*, a La Fontaine fable about a group of mice who enthusiastically agree that the best way to protect themselves against a marauding cat is to tie a bell around its neck. But who's going to put it on? Suddenly they all have their reasons for why it shouldn't be them.

CHAPTER FIFTEEN

IF PEOPLE AND ORGANISMS WERE PRONE TO GETTING SUCKED INTO ALWAYS DEFECT STALEMATES, THEN HOW COULD COOPERATIVE RECIPROCITY EVER BE RESTORED? MORE TO THE POINT, WHAT WERE THE MECHANISMS THAT MADE LIVING THINGS RECIPROCATE ANYWAY?

For anyone who enjoys a satisfying arc to their narratives, a rather neat symmetry was now to turn the game theory story right back to its origins... to the Central European homeland of its first great collaborators, John von Neumann and Oskar Morgenstern.

That's because at some time in 1983 a brilliant chap called Karl Sigmund took over as Head of the Mathematics Department at the University of Vienna (in fact, his office is at 1, Oskar Morgenstern Platz) and he was going to play his part in taking the tale on to its further, final twists.

Sigmund was a noted authority in the field of evolutionary theory, and like so many others, he'd become fascinated by the potential for game theory to define the nuts and bolts of social interaction. As so often, though, he was stumped by how these might actually work.

Vienna was certainly the right place for someone to make a contribution. The great university there had historic form when it came to examining the intersection of biology and mathematics, and many of the world's greatest scientific minds had kicked their theories around in its ancient buildings before going on to make further discoveries in other places.

Gregor Mendel, the Father of Genetics, had studied there in the 1780s (he'd failed his botany exams!) Morgenstern himself had, of course, so had Erwin Schrodinger, and also Kurt Godel - until von Neumann eventually lured him away to Princeton.

Now, just like the famous one-line challenge that Robert Axelrod had set for himself, Karl Sigmund posed a similar question. It was, as he put it in his book, *Games of Life:*

'*Can it ever pay to be nice in a world of selfish individualists?*'

Good question. Most of us are convinced that the way the world works is for the strong types to crush the weak. Axelrod had proved the opposite when he'd shown how cooperation wins by people having multiple partners. But if one was surrounded by defectors, then how did cooperators ever start sharing things out fairly? How were they ever able to do that when there'd be so many greedy people around?

Karl Sigmund thought game theory might make a contribution to answering these questions because, as he put it: 'Mathematical models are playing an ever-increasing role in biology.' His outlook had also been greatly influenced by reading *The Evolution of Cooperation.* Nonetheless, the book's conclusions had mainly applied to humans rather than other life forms because they could use their reasoning mechanisms to act in their own self-interests.

Now Sigmund wanted to see if he could take these rationales on, and to ask whether the same game theoretic decision-making processes might be more or less *universal.* Maybe, he speculated, similar mathematical investigations could unearth whether there were basic reciprocating mechanisms that operated in the natural world in the way they did when researchers studied human subjects?

'More and more frequently, biological problems like, for instance, the dynamics of populations… the emergence of cooperation… evolutionary stable strategies etc., are treated in a spirit more akin to mathematics than to natural science.'
Karl Sigmund, *Games of Life*

As he spent time puzzling over the issue, he'd become great friends with a dazzlingly clever doctoral student of his called Martin Nowak. One day while they were out hiking in the Austrian countryside, he took Nowak right back to Darwin's famous objection to altruism - the most extreme form of cooperation - and then challenged the young man to unpick the reasons why natural selection might appear to rule it out.

Why would they have agreed with Darwin's logic? It was because they both knew that cooperators should theoretically have a lower fitness than defectors, mainly because organisms were taking risks when they reached out for symbiotic associations.

When they did this, they could easily end up being a 'sucker' with no points if they came up against a committed defector in the first exchange. And if they were wiped out then they'd never get the opportunity to establish an iterated game.

Whatever genetic compulsion was making these cooperative acts come about, therefore, it had to be true that many of them went wrong before they could ever get going. Why, therefore, would it ever pay to be cooperative in a world of selfish egoists?

Since these actions were all rolling the survival dice, didn't it suggest that Darwin had to be right, and that their genes could be lost to the gene pool? This conclusion had become very much the accepted historical position, and yet the accumulated results of game theory were pointing towards the *opposite* being true.

If this was the case, Karl Sigmund now tasked his prize student, could he refine Bill Hamilton's explanation for altruism and analyse the reasons for it mathematically? In other words, was Nowak able to pull apart the different biological processes, and 'solve' the prisoner's dilemma in the natural world - in much the same way that Robert Axelrod had done by researching our human logic in his competitions?

Could his young student now use this same approach to show how other life forms had evolved their cooperative strategies?

Martin Nowak (right) and Karl Sigmund...'Can it ever pay to be nice in a world of selfish individualists?'

I don't think it's unfair to say that Martin Nowak became mildly obsessed with the work his boss had set him. Initially in Vienna, and then later at Oxford where he studied under the great Australian theoretical biologist, Bob May, he threw himself headlong into looking for strategies that would get the most points from the iterated prisoner's dilemma. His commitment was so total, he'd later admit, that his wife had to suggest he gave his laptop a rest while they were on their honeymoon.

Like others had before him, he could see that the great strength of Tit for Tat lay in the way it accumulated points by choosing to cooperate with a number of *different* players - but all of them sharing the same collaborative outlook. He was also aware, of course, that there were any number of examples of reciprocal altruism in Nature, both within species and between unrelated ones.

The trouble, however, was that as time had gone on, more and more game theorists were seeing that Tit for Tat had an Achilles heel. This was because *the strategy had no way of correcting a mistaken decision to defect*. And mistakes weren't so strange or unusual either. In fact, they cropped up all the time.

The reason for this was that just as others had before him, Nowak could see that not all defectors were the same. That's because the prisoner's dilemma is like life in reducing behavioural decisions to just a series of binary choices. This is why it had always been difficult for game theorists to make a distinction between 'bad' defectors who are so utterly committed to the idea of competition that they could never bring themselves to be nice... and 'good' defectors who might only have chosen to defect because they'd misjudged their opponents.

What's the core difference between them? It can only be that committed defectors view every exchange as a one-time game. They simply don't understand the idea of trusting people, or of waiting patiently for the scales of reciprocity to be balanced out over time.

On the other hand, the 'trembling hand' defectors have frequently made the wrong choices because they'd become distracted or confused. Wasn't it possible, Nowak now asked himself, that some of these players would actually have preferred to cooperate if they'd only thought about things a bit more, or had a second chance, or even had better information on which they could base their decision?

Humans aren't alone in having the hard-nosed, tough guy types either. Every other organism besides us is committed to its place on the Behavioural Spectrum and, unless they're in a reciprocal arrangement, some of them are *never* going to cooperate. Conflict is encoded in their behaviour. In human terms, don't we see personalities like this rather too much of the time? To certain kinds of people, everything is a fight for what they consider as their *right* to win. While the most extreme of them are often dismissed as sociopathic crackpots - there are many others who have softer shades of presumption.

The problem with Tit for Tat was that it made no distinction between the different reasons for defection choices. The strategy of 'follow the decision of the other man' can actually make things worse because when something plays Defect, it will always be met with a Defect in return. *And if no one gives way, then we and other organisms, and our communities, can get stuck playing Always Defect.*

When this happens in our human societies, we know what miserable, low point scoring, Hobbesian places they can become. If there's no collaboration, they'll quickly descend into horrid and depressing cultures, typified by 'all against all' attitudes, and an overwhelming lack of innovation.

In fact, Bob May himself had set out this scenario in a famous paper in *Nature* in which he showed that mistaken choices to defect could lead to endless retaliation - and, at worst, to never-ending vendettas.

'Without forgiveness life is governed by an endless cycle of resentment and retaliation.'
Roberto Assagioli, *Interview in Psychology Today*

Don't we all recognise this from our own experience? And our human history? Don't we all know how awful feuds can develop between people, and how both sides can end up viewing the idea of peace as impossible? And yet everyone knows they'd all be better off if they weren't so stuck with their Nash Equilibriums.

How was one ever going to restore cooperation if everyone spent their energy on dragging each other down? In short, why, as Karl Sigmund posed it, would anyone or anything ever be nice under these circumstances?

Martin Nowak now decided to revisit Robert Axelrod's tournaments - and more particularly, he began to think through to how similar strategies operated in the natural world. How did anything ever overcome a stalemate?

The answer was that the evolutionary process would occasionally let life forms overcome intractable problems bacause chance mutations would shake up the genetic pot. Sometimes they worked and sometimes they didn't. But when they did find solutions, organisms were taking their decisions blind rather than coming up with a coherent strategy.

Nowak now began to ponder... *if random mutations could unblock evolutionary logjams, perhaps random forgiveness could act in the same way to unblock Tit for Tat's big shortcoming?*

Maybe this suggested it was worth putting out feelers to see if someone had made an error in choosing to Defect - in other words, trying to find out if he'd have preferred to play Cooperate? Was it possible, he wondered, that if one didn't *always* respond to Defect with Defect in return, but sometimes *forgave* and played Cooperate instead, then it would quickly become apparent if the other side wanted to come in from the dark?

Wouldn't doing this give a defector a second chance at reinstating a collaborative relationship?

The more he thought about it, the more he wondered if this might be the way to flush away the solid blockage of Always Defect. But could that be right? Surely forgiving someone had to be a crazy move because doing this risked handing a certain five points to an opponent who wasn't a mistaken softie - but a committed defector instead?

Amazingly, though, Nowak found he'd hit the evolutionary jackpot. He began to see within his computer simulations that the forgiveness gambit could work to one's *advantage.* Yes, there was always the danger of being wrong, but he found that a lot of the time the other side would change their Defect choice, and immediately come back to Cooperate.

In fact, this happened often enough for it to make the idea work. And if the parties began to cooperate again, then they could move on from there to enjoying continuous six-point exchanges, rather than having individuals simply getting one each - and suffering all the downside by being saddled with a reputation for having a zero sum outlook. Taken overall, Nowak found that a metaphorical sigh of relief could go up when a forgiveness play was made instead of a Tit for Tat Defect.

Of course, this kind of departure from Tit for Tat couldn't happen every time someone defected. Forgiveness had to be randomly offered, and it had to be *unexpected.* If it wasn't, defectors would never take any notice of the punishment mechanism that made the strategy so successful. Nowak now went even further than this, and concluded that it might be a mistake to give out any signal at all that handing someone another opportunity was ever on offer.

But random acts, possibly triggered around a third of the time, he concluded, led to the logic of Hawks and Doves being unleashed, and from there to cooperative retaliators eventually restoring Tit for Tat. If the other side wanted to join in, then all they had to do was to play Cooperate in return.

Bingo. Always Cooperate could now set in. And the best bit about this was that the community would now benefit, because the balance of gains would tip towards the group, and away from just suiting a selfish individual.

Nowak was to sum up the power of the forgiveness mechanism in the book he would later write about his findings: *SuperCooperators. Why Cooperation, not Competition is the Key to Life*. As he put it: 'Karl and I took great pleasure in watching (the computer simulations) as Always Defectors weaken and then die out, clearing the way for the triumphant rise of cooperation.' Together, they called the new strategy *Generous Tit for Tat* and described it as: '… never forget a good turn, but occasionally forgive a bad one.' It became widely known in the game theory world as 'Generous'.

Nowak's computer programmes now began to illustrate how, within the great currents of life, winning strategies would bloom and multiply in natural selection. Cast in terms of the Dilemma, successful organisms were those that got the most points, and points meant fitness - and fitness meant offspring. Game theoretic conclusions were showing exactly how 'forgiveness' could arise from the random effects of mutations, and how collaboration would then return and create new opportunities for profitable symbioses.

In human populations, too, the logical trend was also for cooperation to expand. Forgiveness could resolve regretted stand offs. Cooperative choices would grow, and defections would shrink. Just as one sees in trusting societies, Always Cooperate then becomes the uniform exchange.

The price, of course, is that this then leaves the community more open to being exploited by the bad guys, the cheats and fraudulent… and if they're not quickly policed and reduced, their numbers will grow until the defector cycle starts all over again. Martin Nowak was to describe this endless process as: '… in the real world, these cycles could sweep out over years, decades and even centuries… kingdoms come and go. Empires spread, decline and crumble into a dark age. Companies rise up to dominate a market and then fragment and splinter away again in the face of thrusting, innovative competition.'

Nowak could have been describing the conclusions that so many political and military analysts repeatedly come to. Unless the punishment mechanism is employed, then defectors will continue to think they can get away with whatever they choose. They simply view cooperators as too weak and soft to ever fight back.

Hitler and Putin are a couple of good examples. For years each of them were viewed as dangerous opponents - and yet they were forgiven time and again as they snatched at territorial gains and threatened their neighbours. The Doves would look on worriedly, flapping around with sanctions and yet continuing to engage with the Hawks on the other side, endlessly imagining that their collaborative behaviour would somehow wash off on them.

It doesn't. Hawks simply don't understand Doves. And who can blame them for their behavioural decisions if they're continuously forgiven?

From children pushing at their parents to establish boundaries to really bad men with their dreams of empire, it's critical to punish committed defectors, and only to employ forgiveness tactically - and then only if it's later reciprocated.

From this, Nowak went on to make the further point that not only is it necessary to punish defectors, but one has to punish those who also fail to punish them. That's because, when decisions become binary, if a party doesn't join in with the condemnation of selfish behaviour, then they must be condoning it. When this happens, these types have to be confronted before they can form clusters with the serial defector, and become a far more formidable enemy for the Dovish forces.

When Martin Nowak and Karl Sigmund saw through to these conclusions they published their findings in *Nature* in 1992, as *Tit for Tat in Heterogeneous Populations*. In many ways, this would have seemed to be the end of the story. But there was still a kink to come. That was because as Nowak continued his mathematical explorations... he began to see that Generous was only the clear winner when choices were made *sequentially*. Like the small boys and their cake cutting, it only worked when decisions were being made once people knew what the other person had chosen.

But this kind of sequential reasoning was a largely human ability because doing so needed both cognition and imagination. Many of the cooperative phenomena seen in the natural world, however, arise in a different way. Life decisions there are being made *simultaneously*, and this means that the sophistication of the Generous approach generally wouldn't work in Nature. This shortcoming looked like it might kick the idea into touch. But then Nowak had a brainwave and decided to re-examine a strategy that Anatol Rapoport had originally liked, but which he'd later discarded in favour of Tit for Tat.

Rapoport had called his earlier approach 'Simpleton' because it had struck him as too crude a mechanism to ever be successful. Animal behaviourists, however, would later find that it was effective in understanding how ecological alliances worked. What was it? Well, it was nothing more complicated than imagining that organisms were saying to themselves: 'If I'm doing well, I'll keep doing it. If I'm doing badly, I'll change.'

Martin Nowak now had the genius insight to see that the two strategies worked alongside one another. Instead of calling it Simpleton, he described the strategy as 'Win Stay, Lose Shift' and he repeatedly found that it was the winner in simultaneous contests, while Generous carried the day in sequential choices.

Since humans have the unique capacity to react when they've weighed up what others are doing, Bob May was to famously describe the approach in perhaps the greatest of all lessons to come from the iterated prisoner's dilemma: 'You never lose for being too generous!' What a superb conclusion this was to the cold computer logic.

In the non-human world, Nowak was now sure the results were suggesting that theoretical biologists should move their interest away from looking for *stable* strategies and equilibriums, and more towards what he termed '*evolutionary dynamics*'. This was the description that now began to be widely used to explain the way that cycles of cooperation and defection were bound to play out. Each of them, biologists could now see, would inevitably be followed by the other.

Where humans differed from other organisms was that they, alone, would be able to see where they were in the cycle, and therefore what the future would hold if they didn't change things. For Garrett Hardin, selfishness trumped cooperation and life was an inevitable downward cascade with one defection leading to another. For Lin Ostrom, however, people were able to call a halt to being competitive, and to put their heads together and find ways of stopping the feud mechanism of the Tragedy of the Commons from occurring.

By now Martin Nowak's journey as an 'evolutionary mathematician' had taken him from Oxford to the US, and to von Neumann's spiritual home at the Institute for Advanced Studies at Princeton. It was here that he began to refine his approach to 'solving' the Dilemma. Surely, he thought, if he pulled all the different results together, wouldn't it be possible to actually define the different ways that living things had evolved to deal with each other?

However, it was obvious to him that there wouldn't just be one answer because living things have varying levels of intelligence and complexity. Some interaction mechanisms would therefore be shaped at a profound, genetic level, while higher organisms would have developed differently because some would have a larger brain, or like us humans, even the perception and awareness to judge what would be best for itself.

Eventually he was to arrive at *five separate processes* that he believed illustrated how every single life form had evolved to cooperate to its best advantage. These processes, he felt, showed how: '… cooperation is entirely compatible with the hard-boiled arithmetic of survival in an unremittingly cold-eyed and competitive environment. Based on mathematical insights, I have created idealised communities in a computer and charted the conditions in which cooperation can take hold and bloom.'

He was, in short, coming up with the explanation to account for the different ways that organisms arrive at their survival decisions.

If humans formed themselves into well-functioning communities, Nowak said, in which they were capable of resolving their social dilemmas, then they'd display the ability to be using *all five mechanisms*. Other organisms would arguably never be able to employ more than three. It was this difference, he believed, that led members of *Homo sapiens* to be viewed as SuperCooperators.

Why did we have more ways of dealing with each other than other organisms did?

It was because our cultural evolution had grown our brain size, and this had allowed us to develop language, hone our reasoning abilities and to imagine the consequences of our actions. Perhaps most importantly, these advances also led to our facility to climb into another person's head, and to see the world from their perspective.

Lower organisms have never evolved this ability to alter their position on the Behavioural Spectrum. This was why they'd have fewer mechanisms to create cooperative strategies.

So, what did he believe the different methods were?

Well first, he said, there was cooperation based on *Kin Selection*, the extraordinary process that Bill Hamilton had so famously exposed. Using this mechanism allowed living things to recognise family members and to be genetically instructed to collaborate with them, even to the extent of being sterile or sacrificing one's life to let other members pass on their genes.

This has since been described as: '… if you're a relative, I'll scratch your back even if you won't scratch mine.' We humans have plainly inherited the same instinct, and multiple studies show the different ways we so often trust and cluster around close kin. Clearly, at the most profound of levels, we're more likely to trust our genetic family than people we're not related to.

Secondly, he said, there was the mechanism of *Direct Reciprocity* that Robert Trivers had revealed. 'You scratch my back and I'll scratch yours', people called it, and research biologists repeatedly illustrate how the natural world abounds in examples of closely monitored exchanges.

Yes, everyone can see that arrangements like this allow free riders, duckers and takers to defect and take advantage of a collaborative community - but the mechanism still works as long as these wrongdoers are identified and punished. Defecting behaviour will therefore be genetically reduced, because cheats have to pay the ultimate price for their actions by having their fitness adversely affected. Cooperation, on the other hand, is bound to evolve and increase.

Thirdly, though, there's a complex procedure that's only used by us humans. This is the way we package up our experiences of a person's personality and then use our communication skills to describe what they're like. This 'gossiping' is how people end up with their *reputations*, and by passing around our opinions on whether others are trustworthy - and are likely to be so in the future - we're able to unleash what Martin Nowak was to term *Indirect Reciprocity*.

How does it work?

First one needs the brainpower and imagination to assess other people… but also to see that they're assessing us at the same time too. This accounts for why John von Neumann saw us all as players in a vast poker game, motivated to show what our strengths are, and yet trying to hide our weaknesses - even to bluff about them - and so to be endlessly creating impressions about ourselves and our qualities. It means we're all making the best of the cards we hold in our hands, some of which are worth having, and others that are not.

What does this result in? Nothing less than the realisation that we're constantly trading with each other - with our trustworthiness and our individual qualities as the goods we're offering.

We're playing for pretty high stakes as well, and this is what makes us so acutely aware of the importance of our reputations. *It is what people think we have to offer that's so vital.* And because of this, it's become the central component of the reciprocity processes we employ for specialisation and exchange.

This is why it's second nature for us to be always doing things that will bring us rewards at some point in the future. Once Nowak had defined the Indirect Reciprocity mechanism, many of the more sprightly game theorists began referring to it as: 'I'll scratch your back, and someone else will scratch mine.'

Nowak, himself, took a rather more prosaic line and described the process as: 'we help others without expecting an *immediate* return.' But nonetheless, he said, we anticipate others will tell people about how great we are, and this means that we're constantly burnishing our reputations, sometimes by way of our actions, but more generally with our language and other advanced communications skills.

Indirect Reciprocity is the mechanism that so obviously involves weighing each other up, and because this is a complicated process, we need our big brains to keep tabs on where we are in our communities. It's how we keep the score about who owes what to whom, and most importantly, how people are likely to behave in the future, based on how they've behaved in the past.

So powerful can a good reputation be that Dr Nowak's research showed it could even be a deciding factor in a one-time prisoner's dilemma. Logically, you should never cooperate in such a game, but if you really, really trust your instincts that the other person is a dependable, non-zero type, then it might be worth risking it.

Taken together, this all adds up to a highly sophisticated process that's a long way from the tittle-tattle of early hunter-gatherer societies, the obsessions people have about agreeing to hierarchies, and the sending out of mating signals.

Nowak's mathematical reasoning for the risk/reward link in Indirect Reciprocity was that it could only promote cooperation if the probability of knowing someone's reputation exceeded the cost-benefit ratio of the altruistic act. 'I'll risk doing something for you', was what this meant in summary, 'if I believe the good things I've heard about you are true.' As a wise commentator was to say: '... for Direct Reciprocity you need a face. For Indirect - you just need a name.'

Now, if you recall, Bill Hamilton had chillingly summed up the stimulus for highly cooperative acts as 'altruism is just genetic selfishness'. That may be so, Nowak was now saying, but if we want people to think well of us - because it leads to us succeeding in life - then we have to behave in a trusting, empathetic manner. Yes, this behaviour might have had a selfish origin... but who cares? *We cooperate because we want a reputation for cooperating*, and from this we'll end up being part of the networks of cooperators within a society.

Why do we do this? Because we know it's a winning strategy. The evolutionary theorist, Manfred Milinski was to famously sum the process up as: 'Do good and talk about it.' And what is this if it isn't the logic that leads to the evolution of morality? It may not be pleasant to be told we're so calculating about the way we become 'good', but it's nevertheless pleasant to enjoy its benefits.

However, the effort involved in achieving and then maintaining a reputation for being a straight shooter can make it a rocky road. We're 'only human' after all, and who doesn't have bad days? We may want to constantly be kind, honourable, thoughtful and caring people, but who manages to be so wonderful all the time? We're now back with Adam Smith telling us that the way to be 'loved' is to be 'lovely'. Of course, who doesn't try to be that?

But we all know how easy it is to get tired and rattled, to let oneself down, to misunderstand other people's motives, perhaps even to think we're being taken for granted... and we can fail in any one of the thousand and one ways that make us snap from being a committed cooperator to defecting instead.

> '**Humans and other animals make mistakes... become distracted...**
> **suffer mood swings... have a bad day. Nobody's perfect after all.**'
> **Martin Nowak, *SuperCooperators***

Think, for example, about how easy it is to fall out with an old friend. Frequently it's over something that others might consider trivial but which, sadly, can then blow up into a vituperative version of Always Defect. That's because neither side will then back down. Now one can see how vital the forgiveness mechanism of Generous Tit for Tat can be - even if you might never fully recover the trust and reputations that were there before.

The fourth mechanism Nowak listed was a cousin to Indirect Reciprocity in that it extended the same principle to a *group*. The background to this is that genes, we've now come to understand, are the master manipulators for getting their 'vehicles' (that's us and every other organism) to carry them around in as evolutionarily-developed ways as possible. The better the gene can make things, and the fitter the organism is… the more offspring it has. Nowak now called the mechanism *Multilevel Selection*, something that others have summed up as: '… groups that back scratch tend to do better than groups that don't.'

This Multilevel Selection force might stem from individual self-interest, he said, but the effect is to favour social cohesion.

Perhaps the easiest way to explain this is with an example that's cropped up a number of times already - the tricky question about why some animals in a group call out a warning to others when there are predators about. It's seemingly illogical for them to do this because it puts their lives in danger.

Yet this is one of the places where the mechanism of Multilevel Selection shows its place in evolutionary thought because it suggests individuals within clearly defined groups are more likely to support each other - and that this will therefore give them *all* a survival advantage.

When something warns others, but calls attention to itself and therefore puts its own life in danger, it may suffer but the group, nonetheless, benefits from its potential sacrifice.

But the rub is that being unselfish and self-sacrificing doesn't get the altruistic organism killed *every* time it might call out. So, while these heroes might logically be better off if they shut up and let others risk getting eaten, over the course of their lifetimes they're nevertheless more likely to increase their survival chances by taking a full part in group activities.

Plainly they're genetically programmed to take these risks… but behind the actions is the hard maths of a talented oddsmaker. This is because, over evolutionary time, the gene has discovered that being cooperative contributes to a *culture* of collaboration, a way of living, and the non-zero approach of being sacrificial encourages group survival. In short, cooperative groups do best.

Members of colonies with this encoded behaviour survive because they look after each other. And our human lives are no different. Societies that are stuffed with compassionate, loyal, moral and sharing people are the most successful.

But how do these societies develop? Nowak went looking, and eventually found the evidence for it in anthropological research studies. Many of them showed that the stronger the bonds were between group members - and the better they'd done throughout the violent periods of our history - the more the outcome suggested that altruism and morality had grown up alongside the other benefits of cultural evolution.

The individuals in these groups might not have been angels, of course, and they usually had the Big Man's menacing eye on them... but the sharing of information and intelligence, particularly when there was a common language and similar faith memes, led to a collective vision and a general sense of purpose. All these factors would have contributed to making these people prime candidates for the Retaliator Doves that so consistently beat the selfish and egotistical Hawks.

As Martin Nowak was to say, this mechanism gives support to: '... the paradoxical theory that much of human virtue was forged and hardened in the crucible of war.' Where this principle is seen to work best, he believes, is when there are many small groups - and less well when there are a few large ones.

The fifth and last mechanism, according to Nowak, takes place on what he was to term the 'chessboard of life'. By this he's describing the way that just as we're each playing continuous games of prisoner's dilemma with the individuals around us... so they're also playing them with all the people that are around them as well.

By doing this, he says, we create *Spatial Selection* processes in that *we cluster with people like ourselves* - people who agree with our behavioural decisions. When we do this, we're forming little islands of cooperation or defection in an ocean in which others are choosing the opposite approach.

This isn't altogether surprising when one looks around at how we form social networks with people like ourselves. We feel most comfortable when we're helping others in our cultural groupings. There are examples of this wherever one looks... religions are united by having followers with widely held beliefs; companies tend to have people with similar outlooks; clans and tribes are kept together by strong interpersonal bonds; contented nations are made up of people with the same worldviews and loyalties; well-ordered communities generally develop with people holding homogeneous attitudes, and we form friendships with people who think about life in much the same way as we do.

Groupings like these are made up of individuals who understand each other's opinions, hopes and ambitions, and feel most at home when they're together. These kinds of clusters also extend, naturally, to whether people are cooperators or defectors. In a nutshell, whatever the reasons for them might be, these are close-knit groups that are using similar memes to cover their ethical and moral standards.

Nowak now proposed that the linkage between people in these clusters had grown as our cultural history evolved, and we'd formed societies with ever-larger population sizes. Groupings arose particularly with the development of language, the birth of agriculture, the introduction of trading, money, external sources of trust, mass information and so on. All these lurches were squirts of oil in the cooperative process, and each played its part in moving human communities towards increased bottom-up thinking, and further away from the kind of suffocating control the Big Man had always insisted on.

I don't think many of these conclusions would be regarded as original or contentious… but Martin Nowak now tried modelling the relationships mathematically.

Inspired by the *Game of Life* that the British mathematician, John Conway, had set up in 1970, he reasoned that if a person represented a square on a chessboard, then he'd be interacting with the eight squares around him. And the people in each of these would be doing the same thing with the eight that were their neighbours, and so on.

He then gave these players different colours to represent cooperating Doves, defecting Hawks or Retaliator Doves. (John Maynard Smith said the result looked like a 'primordial pizza'.) Nowak then unleashed them to play a gigantic series of prisoner's dilemma games in a computer version of God. This, he said, would show how society behaved in action.

What emerged was a vast and ever-changing landscape of Hawks and Doves that ebbed and flowed as each of them 'underwent cycles of boom and bust'. In his book, *SuperCooperators*, Nowak describes how he watched the myriad squares on his screen erupt as the different behavioural choices dealt with those around them, reproducing how the structure of a population would be affected: 'The result was astounding. These evolutionary games generated irregular or regularly shifting mosaics where strategies of cooperation and defection coexisted in an endlessly milling chaos…(sprouting) a fantastic kaleidoscope of gorgeous patterns, suggestive of lace doilies and stained-glass windows… that seemed to capture the shifting essence of life itself.'

He realised that what he'd reproduced in graphical form was the way that life 'breathes' with zero sum and non-zero groups expanding and then subsiding, each having successful periods followed by losses as the other side exploits their weaknesses. What he was witnessing was the interaction of Hawks and Doves that John Maynard Smith had so brilliantly identified years earlier.

Now Nowak could watch this happening on his computer screen, seeing small numbers of defectors damaging collaborative societies as controlling bullies and dodgy types took advantage of their trust-based environments. With so little opposition, they would rack up their individual five point victories, and grow in numbers to easily out-muscle the clusters of trusting cooperators. Quickly they'd expand to dominate the community.

But with cooperators now reduced to small numbers, the zero sum Hawks would end up fighting each other, and this then allowed retaliation to set in. The cooperators increased in number as they fought the remaining Hawks by becoming Retaliator Doves, using Hawkish tactics, joining up with others like themselves and eventually achieving productive, six point unions. When they grew, so society could return to 'a more obliging way of life.'

As Nowak refined his programmes and pored over the results, a weird thing began to emerge. Even though his colourful images of life were constantly changing, he kept finding that the proportion of cooperators in a population only rarely fell below 32% - the same 'thirdish' proportion that seems to define the point at which the subordinate partners in symbioses feel the deal is worth it.

He showed the result to his mentor, Bob May, and together they agreed that within 'the milling universe of unpredictability and chaos there was one fixed point.' They published the finding in *Nature* to much interest about the way that: '… exploiters and the exploited, cheats and the honest, abusers and abused can coexist, even without the guidance of a strategy.'

Just as Axelrod had found, *you don't need winners to be a winner. Nor do you need a brain.* Things only need to keep dealing with others like themselves and then, as Nowak put it: 'Clusters of cooperators can prevail, even when besieged by defectors.' This, he said, was how Spatial Selection worked and before long he and other researchers were describing it as 'back scratching tends to bring back-scratchers together.'

What's the significance of these mutually supportive groups in our human lives? Very considerable seems to be the conclusion, because they provide the glue that holds societies together. Some commentators even see them as having the same level of importance as family ties, because they obviously create social bonds between individuals.

We humans illustrate this by being at our happiest in networks. Even though they might be as tenuous as sharing a hobby, liking similar fashions, being a fan of the same singer or sports team, reading a certain newspaper, or simply being neighbours in the same street, we feel an affinity with those who share our lives and interests.

We're most comfortable when we're clustered with others in clans or tribes. These operate even if they're as artificial as things like clubs, schools or university friendships, getting together with people of similar backgrounds or like-minded attitudes, having the same religious beliefs, the same loyalties, or perhaps just some kind of historical connection. Martin Nowak was to sum this up in an interview when he said: 'The reality is that I'm much more likely to interact with my friends, and they're much more likely to interact with their friends.'

The likelihood is that our instinctive search for cooperative relationships is guided by the kinds of reputations that lead us to think someone is *trustworthy*. In other words, they're like us. And this correlates closely with people who share our outlooks.

Nowak described these networks as acting like diseases in that they infect one another with the same sense of belonging. Research even suggests that happy people fall into this same category as they often cluster together, reinforcing each other's sunny view of the world and adding to their group's overall happiness in the process.

> 'The way that we human beings collaborate is as clearly described by mathematics as the descent of the apple that fell in Newton's garden.'
> Martin Nowak, *SuperCooperators*

As our cultural evolution has shown, humans have always relied on copying people that we regard as successful. It's for this reason that we adore celebrities in spite of their flaws. We idolise sporting heroes, respect the rich and famous and have the highest regard for anyone we think is on a fast track to heaven. We probably cluster around these images and relationships because, at some profound level, we equate their perceived success with the mate selection mechanisms that were so vital to us all those millennia ago.

When he'd boiled down the game theoretic outcomes of these 'imitating' relationships, Nowak concluded that there must be a deep linkage between the degree of cooperation in a community and the structure of its internal networks.

His mathematical insights went even further. If there were reasons, he concluded, for linking a few close friends within a society, then cooperators would always outnumber defectors. In fact, he continued, since the strength of these relationships increases with intimacy, the fewer the number there are, the more you'd share your fate with them.

How odd that it had taken forty years of game theory research to tell us what we instinctively know about human progress… that it's always small groups of highly committed people who will alter the course of history. Conspirators have always been the people who bring about change, tight teams lead corporate restructures, a few warrior types win wars, Christ chose just twelve followers, political cabinets have limited members, crack military squads are tiny. As Martin Nowak was to say, there were three musketeers, not three hundred.

These groups are at their most powerful when their networks overlap, something that happens when people show that they have choices in common, and are therefore predisposed to cooperate.

Two hundred and fifty years before Nowak had arrived at his findings, Adam Smith had come to very similar conclusions without so much as an abacus, never mind the computer modelling of evolutionary game theorists. Smith was to later explain that he'd twice changed his mind about how he thought these social clusters worked.

At first, he'd reasoned that individuals with similar views and standards would have enough common interest in the future to make them get together and create a society that excluded destructive people. But any observation of people's behaviour suggested to him that this actually didn't happen. Yes, you'd think it should, but disappointingly it tends not to.

This then led him to conclude that since society arose as the result of people acting in their own self-interest, then a cooperative community was simply a by-product of efficient market forces. Yet again, though, he decided that human history didn't support the view.

Finally, he arrived at the conviction that since people with the strongest bonds between them would naturally group together into clusters in which individuals shared the same convictions, then they'd 'precipitate out' of societies they didn't like.

Once they'd left, they would then form wholly new communities of people who had the same beliefs as themselves.

No doubt if Smith had understood the language of game theory, he'd have said that these cooperative types might not pass through the Retaliator Dove stage at all, but would simply up sticks and go, leaving the 'selfish rationalist' zero summers to fight it out amongst themselves. The cooperators would then set up a new society somewhere else, leaving the Hawkish, defector people to wither and fail as a result.

Nice people, for instance, frequently don't solve the problems of their neighbourhood, they simply move to a district with a more agreeable bunch of citizens. The ones they've left behind then go progressively downhill. This is, for example, being seen on a large scale as one of the most significant social trends in the US, where people are leaving states with high taxes and regulation, widespread crime and lower economic freedoms to migrate to others with a more dynamic and collaborative outlook.

The same thing is happening around the world as people flee rather than fight, often becoming refugees in the process. 20% of Venezuelans, for instance, have given up on their homeland, large numbers of young Russians have as well, similarly over half of all Syrians, and many from the more badly governed countries in Africa. Just like the mice in the Belling the Cat fable, they've decided to leave the cat to its own destructive path - and to start somewhere new.

Adam Smith had been seeing the same forces at work… that the bonds between cooperators lead to gains. It's simply people following the core principle of life, and creating 1+1=3. That's why, as Martin Nowak concluded, cooperation was the key. Just as Kropotkin and Maynard Smith had argued, so Nowak now saw the same pattern being proven mathematically in his evolutionary dynamics.

All these great thinkers had arrived at the same point: that cooperation had existed throughout the whole story of life on earth. It was the same force that had even led atoms to form molecules to achieve greater stability, made elements combine to create compounds, compounds to form molecules and from there, somehow, to arrive at the self-replicating mechanisms and cellular life from which we've all descended.

It was also the force that's been behind evolution's endless search for symbioses, ecological unions, genetically dictated altruism and every other kind of non-zero, cooperative strategy. All these were based on the drive to combine energy so that life can resist the forbidding certainty of the 2nd Law of Thermodynamics.

'The 2nd Law that entropy always increases holds, I
think, the supreme position among the laws of nature.'
Sir Arthur Eddington, *The Nature of the Physical World*

This is how life was built - and it is how things survive. But what a long ride it's been, an extraordinary story - and yet it's always had the same underlying direction

What does it all mean? What do these forces suggest for us humans? Have they allowed us to understand a bit more about ourselves? Or have they just added to the confusion?

Picture Credits:

Cover and end papers: Details from Pink Beach Towel by Bruce McLean. Copyright, the artist. Published by CCA Galleries, London and printed by Coriander Studios. Reproduced by kind permission of Bruce McLean and the CCA Galleries, September, 2022

Introduction: Alamy
Chapter 1:   Alamy, DreamWorks Pictures/ Paramount Pictures
Chapter 2:   www.CartoonStock.com, Alamy
Chapter 3:   Alamy, Source unknown
Chapter 4:   Alamy, Shutterstock/AP
Chapter 5:   iStock/Getty Images, Source unknown/ c Universal/Alamy
Chapter 6:   Alamy, Source unknown
Chapter 7:   Source unknown
Chapter 8:   Source unknown, Alamy
Chapter 9:   Getty Images
Chapter 10:   Alamy, Shutterstock/ Source unknown
Chapter 11:   Alamy
Chapter 12:   Source unknown
Chapter 13:   Source unknown, BBC Archives
Chapter 14:   Getty Images, Isaac Lash/Press Herald
Chapter 15:   Alamy, Franz Johann Morgenbesser/Flickr